DER ROSENKAVALIER

(THE ROSE-BEARER)

Comedy for Music in Three Acts by
HUGO VON HOFMANNSTHAL
(English Version by ALFRED KALISCH)

Music by

RICHARD STRAUSS

Op. 59

Price, $1.00

Fürstner Limited, London, W.1

Sole Selling Agents for U. S. A.

BOOSEY & HAWKES Inc.
New York, N. Y.

SYNOPSIS

The play begins with a scene in a chamber of the Princess von Werdenberg's Vienna residence in the early years of the reign of Maria Theresa. The Princess reclines on a sofa half embraced by the ardent Octavian, who professes an all consuming love for her. In the midst of this impassioned scene the lovers are disturbed by sounds which the indiscreet ones fear are the footsteps and the voice of the Prince von Werdenberg, returning unexpectedly from hunting. Octavian quickly conceals himself and dons the dress of a lady's maid, and the anxiety of the Princess is changed to amusement when the noisy, boastful and debauched Baron Ochs of Lerchenau unceremoniously enters the chamber to crave the assistance of the Princess in his forthcoming marriage with Sophia Faninal. The old rake no sooner sets eyes on Octavian disguised as a maid than he makes love to her and invites her to sup with him. Meanwhile the Princess, as was the practice of ladies of quality in those days, has her morning interview with her attorney, head cook, milliner, hairdresser, literary adviser, animal dealer, etc., including a flute player and an Italian tenor, whose business it is to help divert her.

When Baron Lerchenau departs the Princess asks Octavian to be the bearer of the silver rose which the bridegroom left with her to be delivered to the bride, Sophia, according to the custom of those days. The first act ends a little sadly when the Princess reflects on the day not distant when her charm shall have faded and her power to attract her lover shall have passed away.

In the second act Sophia in her home receives the silver rose sent to her by the Princess in behalf of Baron Lerchenau. Unfortunately for the Baron, Octavian no sooner delivers the rose, and Sophia no sooner receives it, than the two fall desperately in love with each other. In the midst of their new-found joy the Baron enters to be formally presented to his betrothed and to have the contract duly drawn and signed. His impudent manner and loose language disgust Sophia. Octavian picks a quarrel with him, draws his sword and wounds him in the hand. Sophia weeps and protests she will never marry the Baron. Faninal fumes and rages, declaring his daughter shall marry the Baron or take the veil, for he is socially ambitious and seeks to link his wealth as a merchant with an aristocratic house. Octavian sets his wits to work and the third act of the play puts everything to rights.

Disguised as the maid of the Princess he makes and keeps an appointment with the Baron, at an inn. There so many tricks are played on the Baron that he thinks he has lost his reason and is in a madhouse. Faces appear in unsuspected panels; a widow enters claiming him as her husband; children rush in and hail him as "papa"; the commissary of police arrests him on a charge of leading young girls astray; and in his attempt to clear himself, he makes a hopeless muddle of it all and is rightfully disgraced. The merchant, Faninal, is furious to find his prospective son-in-law in such a brawl, and Sophia publicly renounces him. The arrival of the Princess is the signal for the police to withdraw and for Octavian to reveal himself to the Baron in his usual garments of a man.

And so the play ends, happily, although there is a little bitter in the cup of the Princess as she sees her lover so soon another's prize. The love of the Princess for the boy was but a passing romance, innocent enough, though indiscreet, but it supplies the shadow to the lovely picture of Octavian and Sophia locked in each other's arms when the comedy is done.

CHARACTERS

PRINCESS VON WERDENBERG (*Wife of Field*
  Marshal Prince von Werdenberg) . . . *Soprano*
BARON OCHS OF LERCHENAU . . . . . *Bass*
OCTAVIAN (*called Mignon—a Young Gentleman of*
  Noble Family) . . . . . . *Mezzo-Soprano*
HERR VON FANINAL (*a Rich Merchant, Newly*
  Ennobled) . . . . . . *High Baritone*
SOPHIA (*His Daughter*) . . . . . *High Soprano*
MISTRESS MARIANNE LEITMETZER
  (*Duenna*) . . . . *High Soprano*
VALZACCHI (*a Man of Affairs*) . . . . . *Tenor*
ANNINA (*His Partner*) . . . . . . *Alto*
A COMMISSARY OF POLICE . . . . . *Bass*
MAJOR-DOMO OF THE PRINCESS . . . *Tenor*
MAJOR-DOMO OF FANINAL . . . . . *Tenor*
THE PRINCESS'S ATTORNEY . . . . . *Bass*
LANDLORD . . . . *Tenor*
A SINGER . . . . *High-Tenor*
A SCHOLAR
A FLUTE PLAYER
A HAIRDRESSER
HIS ASSISTANT
A WIDOW OF NOBLE FAMILY
THREE ORPHANS OF NOBLE { *Soprano*
  FAMILY . . . . . . { *Mezzo-Soprano*
                      { *Alto*
A MILLINER . . . . *Soprano*
A VENDOR OF ANIMALS . . . . . *Tenor*
FOUR FOOTMEN OF THE PRINCESS { *Two Tenor*
                             { *Two Bass*
FOUR WAITERS . . . . . { *One Tenor*
                        { *Three Bass*

A Little Black Boy, Footmen, Couriers, Heyducks, Cookboys,
Guests, Musicians, Two Watchmen, Four Little Children,
Various Personages of suspicious appearance.

PLACE OF ACTION:
Vienna, in the early years of the reign of Maria Theresa.

ERSTER AUFZUG

Das Schlafzimmer der Feldmarschallin. Links im Alkoven das grosse zeltförmige Himmelbett. Neben dem Bett ein dreiteiliger chinesischer Wandschirm, hinter dem Kleider liegen. Ferner ein kleines Tischchen und ein paar Sitzmöbel. Auf einem Fauteuil links liegt ein Degen in der Scheide. Rechts grosse Flügeltüren in das Vorzimmer. In der Mitte kaum sichtbar kleine Türe in die Wand eingelassen. Sonst keine Türen. In dem Alkoven rechts steht ein Frisiertisch und ein paar Sessel an der Wand. Fauteuils und zwei kleine Sofas. Die Vorhänge des Bettes sind zurückgeschlagen. Octavian kniet auf einem Schemel vor dem Sofa links und hält die Feldmarschallin, die in der Sofaecke liegt, halb umschlungen. Man sieht ihr Gesicht nicht, sondern nur ihre sehr schöne Hand und den Arm, von dem das Spitzenhemd abfällt. Durch das halfgeöffnete Fenster strömt die helle Morgensonne herein. Man hört im Garten Vöglein singen.

OCTAVIAN: Wie du warst! Wie du bist!
              Das weiss niemand, das ahnt keiner!

MARSCHALLIN *(richtet sich in den Kissen auf)*:
              Beklagt Er sich über das, Quinquin? Möcht' Er, dass
                              viele das wüssten?

OCTAVIAN *(feurig)*:
              Engel! Nein! Selig bin ich,
              Dass ich der Einzige bin, der weiss, wie du bist.
              Keiner ahnt es! Niemand weiss es!
              Du, du—was heisst das "Du"? Was "du und ich"?
              Hat denn das einen Sinn?
              Das sind Wörter, blosse Wörter, nicht? Du sag'!
              Aber dennoch: Es ist etwas in ihnen,
              ein Schwindeln, ein Ziehen, ein Sehnen und Drängen,
              ein Schmachten und Brennen:
              Wie jetzt meine Hand zu deiner Hand kommt,
              Das Zudirwollen, das Dichumklammern,
              das bin ich, das will zu dir;
              aber das Ich vergeht in dem Du . . .
              Ich bin dein Bub', aber wenn mir dann Hören und Sehen
                                   vergeht—
            wo ist dann dein Bub?

MARSCHALLIN *(leise)*:
              Du bist mein Bub', du bist mein Schatz!
                                (Sehr innig).
            Ich hab' dich lieb!

OCTAVIAN *(fährt auf)*:
              Warum ist Tag? Ich will nicht den Tag! Für was ist
                                der Tag!
            Da haben dich alle! Finster soll sein!
(Er stürzt ans Fenster, schliesst es und zieht die Vorhänge zu. Man hört von fern ein leises Klingeln.)

MARSCHALLIN *(lacht leise)*:

OCTAVIAN: Lachst du mich aus?

ACT ONE

The bedroom of the Princess. In the alcove to the left the large, tent-shaped fourposter. Next the bed a threefold screen, behind which clothes are scattered to the ground. A small table, chairs, etc. To the right, folding doors leading to the bedchamber. In the centre, scarcely visible, a little door let into the wall. No other doors. Between the alcove and the small door, a toilet table and some armchairs against the wall. The curtains of the bed are half drawn. Through the half-open window the morning sun streams in. From the garden sounds the song of birds. Octavian kneels on a footstool, half embracing the Princess who is reclining in the bed. Her face is hidden, only her beautiful hand is seen, and her arm peeping from out the sleeve of her night gown of lace.

OCTAVIAN (*rapturously*):

    All thy soul, all thy heart—
    Their perfections who can measure?

PRINCESS: Why grieve so sorely at that, Mignon,
    Should they be known on the housetops?

OCTAVIAN (*passionately*):

    Angel! No! Blessed am I
    That it is I, I alone who know their secrets.
    Who can measure such perfection?
    Thou, thou, thou! What means that "Thou?"
    That "Thou and I,"
    Have they meaning or sense?—
    They are merely empty nothings. What? O say.
    Yet have they something,
    Yea, a something is in them
    That craveth, that urgeth, that striveth,
    That fainteth and yearneth.
    To thine my hand thus its way hath found:
    And this quest for thee, and this clinging —
    That am I, who seek thee out
    Mingling with thee and lost in that "Thou."
    I am thy Boy; but when reft of all senses I lie in thy arms.
    Where then is thy Boy?

PRINCESS: Thou art my Boy. Thou art my love. I love thee so.

OCTAVIAN: Why dawneth day? How hateful is day. What availeth
                             the day?
    Then all men can see thee. Dark let it be.

    (*He rushes to the window and closes it. A bell is heard ringing softly
    in the distance. The Princess smiles to herself.*)

    Smil'st thou at me?

7

MARSCHALLIN (*zärtlich*):
Lach' ich dich aus?

OCTAVIAN: Engel!

MARSCHALLIN: Schatz du, mein junger Schatz! ..
(*Wieder ein leises Klingeln.*)
Horch!

OCTAVIAN: Ich will nicht.

MARSCHALLIN: Still, pass auf!

OCTAVIAN: Ich will nichts hören! Was wird's denn sein?
(*Das Klingeln näher.*)
Sind's leicht Laufer mit Briefen und Komplimenten?
Vom Saurau, vom Hartig, vom portugieser Envoyé?
Hier kommt mir keiner herein. Hier bin ich der Herr!

(*Die kleine Tür in der Mitte geht auf und ein kleiner Neger in Gelb, behängt mit silbernen Schellen, ein Präsentierbrett mit der Schokolade tragend, trippelt über die Schwelle. Die Tür hinter dem Neger wird von unsichtbaren Händen geschlossen.*)

MARSCHALLIN: Schnell, da versteck' Er sich! Das Frühstück ist's.

OCTAVIAN (*gleitet hinter den vorderen Wandschirm*):

MARSCHALLIN: Schmeiss' Er doch Seinen Degen hinters Bett.

OCTAVIAN (*fährt nach dem Degen und versteckt ihn*):

MARSCHALLIN: (*verschwindet hinter den Bettvorhängen, die sie fallen lässt.*)

DER KLEINE NEGER (*stellt das Servierbrett auf das kleine Tischchen, schiebt dieses nach vorne, neben das linksstehende Sofa, verneigt sich dann tief gegen das Bett, die kleinen Arme über die Brust gekreutzt. Dann tanzt er zierlich nach rückwärts, immer das Gesicht dem Bette zugewandt. An der Tür verneigt er sich nochmals und verschwindet*).

MARSCHALLIN (*tritt zwischen den Bettvorhängen hervor. Sie hat einen leichten mit Pelz verbrämten Mantel umgeschlagen*).

OCTAVIAN (*kommt zwischen der Mauer und dem Wandschirm hervor*).

MARSCHALLIN: Er Katzenkopf, Er Unvorsichtiger!
Lässt man in einer Dame Schlafzimmer seinen Degen
herumliegen?
Hat Er keine besseren Gepflogenheiten?

OCTAVIAN: Wenn Ihr zu dumm ist, wie ich mich benehm',
und wenn Ihr abgeht, dass ich kein Geübter in solchem
Sachen bin,
dann weiss ich überhaupt nicht, was Sie an mir hat!

MARSCHALLIN (*zärtlich, auf dem Sofa*):
Philosophier' Er nicht, Herr Schatz, und komm Er her.
Jetzt wird gefrühstückt. Jedes Ding hat seine Zeit.

OCTAVIAN (*setzt sich dicht neben sie. Sie frühstücken sehr zärtlich. Octavian legt sein Gesicht auf ihr Knie. Sie streichelt sein Haar. Er blickt zu ihr auf. Leise*):
Marie Theres'!

PRINCESS: Smile I at thee?

OCTAVIAN: Angel!

PRINCESS: Dearest, my dearest Boy!

(Bell again.)

Hark!

OCTAVIAN: I will not!

PRINCESS: Hush, beloved!

OCTAVIAN: Deaf and blind I.   What can it be?

(The tinkling grows more distinct.)

Is it couriers with letters and declarations?
From Sauvan and Hartig or the Portuguese Ambassador?
I hold the door against the world.   I am master here.

PRINCESS: Quick!   Go conceal yourself.   My chocolate!

(The little door in the centre is opened and a small black boy in yellow, with silver bells, carrying a silver salver with chocolate, enters with mincing steps.   The door is closed behind him by unseen hands.   Octavian slips behind the screen.)

PRINCESS: Foolish Boy!   Hide your sword and do not stir!

(Octavian reaches after the sword and hides it.)

(The boy puts the salver on one of the small tables, moves it to the front of the stage and places the sofa next to it, bows to the Princess with his hands crossed over his breast, then dances away backward with his face always towards his mistress; at the door he bows again and disappears.)

(The Princess appears from behind the curtains of the bed.   She has wrapped round her a light dressing gown edged with fur.)

(Octavian reappears from behind the screen.)

PRINCESS: You featherhead!   You careless Good for Naught!
Is it allowed to leave a sword lying in the room of a lady
                                of fashion?
Where have you learnt to show such lack of breeding?

OCTAVIAN: Well, if my breeding be not to your taste,
If it displease you that in scenes like this my skill is far
                                to seek
Then truly it were better to bid you farewell.

PRINCESS: *(tenderly from the sofa)*:

Cease your philosophizing, Sir, and come to me.   Now let
                us breakfast.   Everything in its own time.

(Octavian seats himself close to her.   They breakfast.   He puts his head on her lap; she strokes his hair.)

OCTAVIAN: Marie Theres'!

9

MARSCHALLIN: Octavian!

OCTAVIAN: Bichette!

MARSCHALLIN: Quinquin!

OCTAVIAN: Mein Schatz!

MARSCHALLIN: Mein Bub'!

(Sie früstücken weiter.)

OCTAVIAN *(lustig)*:
Der Feldmarschall sitzt im krowatischen Wald
und jagt auf Bären und Luchsen.
Und ich, ich setz' hier, ich junges Blut, und jag' auf was?
Ich hab' ein Glück, ich hab' ein Glück!

MARSCHALLIN *(indem ein Schatten über ihr Gesicht fliegt)*:
Lass Er den Feldmarschall in Ruh'!
Mir hat von ihm geträumt.

OCTAVIAN: Heut nacht hat dir von ihm deträumt? Heut Nacht?

MARSCHALLIN: Ich schaff' mir meine Träume nicht an.

OCTAVIAN: Heut Nacht hat dir von deinem Mann geträumt? Heut
Nacht?

MARSCHALLIN: Mach' Er nicht solche Augen. Ich kann nichts dafür.
Er war auf einmal wieder zu Haus.

OCTAVIAN *(leise)*:
Der Feldmarschall?

MARSCHALLIN: Es war ein Lärm im Hof von Pferd' und Leut' und er
war da,
Vor Schreck war ich auf einmal wach, nein, schau' nur,
schau' nur, wie kindisch ich bin: ich hör' noch immer
den Rumor im Hof.
Ich bring's nicht aus dem Ohr. Hörst du leicht auch was?

OCTAVIAN: Ja freilich hör' ich was, aber muss es denn dein Mann
sein!?
Denk' dir doch, wo der ist: im Raitzenland, noch hinter-
wärts von Esseg.

MARSCHALLIN: Ist das sicher sehr weit?
Na, dann wird's halt was anders sein. Dann ist's ja gut.

OCTAVIAN: Du schaust so ängstlich drein, Theres!

MARSCHALLIN: Weiss Er, Quinquin—wenn es auch weit ist—
Der Feldmarschall ist halt sehr geschwind. Einmal—
(Sie stockt.)

OCTAVIAN *(eifersüchtig)*:
Was war einmal?

MARSCHALLIN *(zerstreut, horcht)*.

OCTAVIAN: Was war einmal? Bichette!
Bichette! Was war einmal?

MARSCHALLIN: Ach sei Er gut, Er muss nicht alles wissen.

OCTAVIAN *(wirft sich verzweifelt aufs Sofa rechts)*:
So spielt Sie sich mit mir! Ich bin ein unglücklicher
Mensch!

10

PRINCESS: Octavian!

OCTAVIAN: Bichette!

PRINCESS: Mignon!

OCTAVIAN: Belovéd.

PRINCESS: My Boy!

OCTAVIAN: The Field Marshal, he stays in far Croatian wilds, a hunt-
                  ing for brown bears and black boars,
            And I in the flower of my youth, stay here, hunting for
                  what?
            Happy am I! Happy am I!

PRINCESS (*a shadow passing over her face*):
            But, let the Marshal be in peace.   I dreamed a dream of
                  him this night.

OCTAVIAN: This night you dreamed a dream of him? This night?

PRINCESS: My dreams are not mine to command.

OCTAVIAN: You dreamed a dream this very night of him?   The
                  Prince?

PRINCESS: Why look so sad and angry?   'Tis no fault of mine...
            My husband was at home again.

OCTAVIAN: Your husband here?

PRINCESS: There was a noise without of horse and man—and he was
                  here.
            For fright I started up in haste—Now look you,
            Now look you what a child I am—still I can hear it, all
                  the noise without.
            'Tis ringing in my ears, do you not hear it?

OCTAVIAN: Yes, truly, sounds I hear: but why think it must be your
                  husband?
            Think but where he's a-hunting — far away,
            At Esseg or a score of leagues beyond.

PRINCESS: Is he so far, think you?

OCTAVIAN: Then something else it is we hear, and all is well,
            You look so full of fear, Theres'.

PRINCESS: But see, Mignon, though it be distant,
            The Prince at times can travel wond'rous fast; for once—

OCTAVIAN: What did he, once?   What did he, once?   What did he,
                  once?
            Bichette, Bichette!   What did he, once?

PRINCESS: Oh, let him be—why should I tell you all things?

OCTAVIAN: See how she flouts my love!
                  (*Throws himself in despair on to the sofa.*)
            Why will you drive me to despair?

11

MARSCHALLIN (*horcht*) :

Jetzt trotz' Er nicht. Jetzt gilt's: es ist der Feldmarschall.
Wenn es ein Fremder wär', so wär der Lärm da draussen
in meinen Vorzimmer.
Es muss mein Mann sein, der durch die Garderob' herein
will
Und mit den Lakaien disputiert.
Quinquin, es ist mein Mann!

OCTAVIAN (*fährt nach seinem Degen und läuft gegen rechts*).

MARSCHALLIN : Nicht dort, dort ist das Vorzimmer.
Da sitzen meine Lieferanten und ein halbes Dutzend
Lakaien.
Da!

OCTAVIAN (*läuft hinüber zur kleinen Türe*).

MARSCHALLIN : Zu spät! Sie sind schon in der Garderob'!
Jetzt bleibt nur eins!
Versteck' Er sich!
(*Nach einer kurzen Pause der Ratlosigkeit.*)
Dort!

OCTAVIAN : Ich spring' ihm in den Weg! Ich bleib' bei dir.

MARSCHALLIN : Dort hinters Bett! Dort in der Vorhäng! Und **rühr'**
dich nicht!

OCTAVIAN (*zögernd*) :

Wenn er mich dort erwischt, was wird aus **dir**,
Theres'?

MARSCHALLIN (*flehend*) :

Versteck' Er sich, mein Schatz.

OCTAVIAN (*beim Wandschirm*) :

Theres!
(*Er verschwindet zwischen dem Wandschirm und der Alkovenwand.*)

MARSCHALLIN (*ungeduldig aufstampfend*) :

Sei Er ganz still!

(*Mit blitzenden Augen.*)

Das möcht' ich sehn,
Ob einer sich dort hinüber traut, wenn ich hier steh'.
Ich bin kein napolitanischer General: wo ich steh', steh'
ich.
Sind brave Kerl'n, meine Lakaien, wollen ihn nich herein
lassen,
sagen, dass ich schlaf'. Sehr brave Kerl'n!

(*Aufhorchend.*)

Die Stimm'!
Das ist ja gar nicht die Stimm' vom Feldmarschall!
Sie sagen "Herr Baron" zu ihm! Das ist ein Fremder.

(*Lustig.*)

Quinquin, es ist ein Besuch.

(*Sie lacht.*)

12

PRINCESS : Command yourself. 'Tis true. It is the Prince indeed.
For were a stranger here, the noise would surely be there
in the antechamber.
It is my husband. I hear his footsteps in the closet.
In vain the lackeys bar his way. Mignon, it is the Prince.
(*Octavian draws his sword and runs to the right.*)
Not there, there is the antechamber.
There, sure, a crowd with wares to offer, and a score of
lackeys are in waiting.
There!
(*Points to the small door. Octavian runs in that direction.*)
Too late! I hear them in the closet now. There's but one
chance.
Conceal yourself!
(*After a brief pause of helplessness.*)
There!

OCTAVIAN : I will not let him pass: I stay with you!

PRINCESS : There— by the bed—there in the curtains! And do not
move!

OCTAVIAN (*hesitating*) :
Should I be caught by him, what fate is yours, Theres'!

PRINCESS : (*pleading*) :
Conceal yourself, beloved.
(*Stamping her foot impatiently.*)

OCTAVIAN (*by the screen*) :
Theres'—

PRINCESS : Quick now, be still!
Now let me see who dares to stir one inch towards the
door
While I am here.
I'm no faint-hearted Italian brigadier.
Where I stand, stand I.
(*She walks energetically towards the little door and listens.*)
They're worthy fellows, keeping guard without there,
vowing they'll not make way for him,
Vowing I sleep—most worthy fellows—
(*The noise in the anteroom grows louder.*)
That voice
(*Listens.*)
That is not, truly, no, 'tis not my husband's voice.
'Tis Baron that they're calling him: 'Tis a stranger!
(*Laughing.*)
Mignon, it is someone else.

13

Fahr' Er schnell in seine Kleider,
aber bleib' Er versteckt,
dass die Lakaien Ihn nicht seh'n.
. Die blöde grosse Stimm' müsste ich doch kennen.
Wer ist denn das? Herrgott, das ist der Ochs.
Das ist mein Vetter, der Lerchenau, der Ochs auf Ler-
chenau,
Was will denn der? Jesus Maria!
(Sie muss lachen.)
Quinquin, hört Er,
Quinquin, erinnert Er sich nicht?
Vor fünf oder sechs Tagen—den Brief—
Wir sind im Wagen gesessen,
und einen Brief haben sie mir an den Wagenschlag
gebracht.
Das war der Brief vom Ochs.
Und ich hab' keine Ahnung, was drin gestanden ist.
(Lacht.)
Daran ist Er allein schuld, Quinquin!

Stimme des Haushofmeisters *(draussen)*:
Belieben Euer Gnaden in der Galerie zu warten!
(Die kleine rückwärtige Türe wird während des Folgenden mehr-
mals bis zum Spalt geöffnet und wieder geschlossen, als wollte
von aussen jemand eindringen, dem von anderen der Eintritt
verwehrt wird.)
Stimme des Barons *(draussen)*:
Wo hat Er seine Manieren galernt?
Der Baron Lerchenau antichambrieret nicht.
Marschallin: Quinquin, was treibt Er denn? Wo steckt Er denn?
Octavian *(in einen Frauenrock und Jäkchen, das Haar mit einem*
Schnupftuch und einem Bande wie in einem Häubchen, tritt
hervor und knickst):
Befehl'n fürstli' Gnad'n i bin halt noch nit recht lang
in fürstli'n Dienst.
Marschallin: Du, Schatz!
Und nicht einmal mehr als ein Busserl kann ich dir geben.
(Küsst ihn schnell. Neuer Lärm draussen.)
Er bricht mir ja die Tür ein, der Herr Vetter.
Mach' Er, dass Er hinauskomm'.
Schleich Er frech durch die Lakaien durch.
Er ist ein blitzgescheiter Lump! Und komm' Er wieder,
Schatz,
aber in Mannskleidern und durch die vordre Tür, wenn's
Ihm beliebt.
(Setzt sich auf das Sofa links mit dem Rücken gegen die Tür und
beginnt ihre Schokolade zu trinken. Octavian geht schnell gegen
die kleine Tür und will hinaus. Im gleichen Augenblick wird
die Tür aufgerissen, und Baron Ochs, den die Lakaien vergeblich
abzuhalten suchen, tritt ein. Octavian, der mit gesenktem Kopf
rasch entwischen wollte, stösst mit ihm zusammen. Dann drückt
er sich verlegen an die Wand links von der Tür. Drei Lakaien
sind gleichzeitig mit dem Baron eingetreten, stehen ratlos.)

14

Now to escape will be quite easy.
But in hiding' remain,
That the footmen do not see you.
That loutish, foolish voice, surely too well I know it—
Mon Dieu! 'tis Ochs, I do protest, my cousin of Lerchenau
'Tis Ochs of Lerchenau. What can he seek? But stay:
I have it—

> (*Bursts into a laugh.*)

Listen, Mignon, you cannot have forgot

> (*Going a few steps towards the left.*)

The league-long letter that they brought
When I was in my coach (you were with me)—
Some five days since, starting for Court, and I scarce
> looked at it.
That letter came from Ochs.
And now I have no inkling what my Cousin said.
See to what evil ways, Mignon, you lead me!

VOICE OF THE MAJOR-DOMO (*without*):
> Will your Lordship be pleased to attend in the gallery?

VOICE OF THE BARON (*without*):
> Where did you learn to treat a nobleman thus? A Baron
> Lerchenau cannot be waiting.

PRINCESS: Mignon, where are you hid? What tricks are these?

OCTAVIAN: (*in a skirt and a short jacket, with his hair tied with a kerchief and ribbon to look like a cap, comes from behind the screen and curtseys*):
> An't please you, your Highness,
> I've not long been of your Highness' household here.

PRINCESS: Sweetheart, and only one kiss may I give you,
One only, my dearest.
> (*Kisses him quickly*
My noble kinsman's battering all the doors down.
Now as quickly as may be
March boldly past the footman there.
'Tis sport for brazen rogues like you! And come back
> soon, beloved,
In your own habit, and through the main door, as a gentleman should.

(*The Princess sits down with her back to the door and begins to sip her chocolate. Octavian goes quickly towards the little door and tries to go out, but at that moment the door is flung open, and Baron Ochs, whom the footmen vainly try to keep back, forces his way in. Octavian, who attempts to escape, hiding his face, runs into him. Then, in confusion, he stands aside against the wall, to the left of the door. Three footmen enter with the Baron and stand hesitating what to do.*)

BARON (*mit Grandezza zu den Lakaien*):
Selbstverständlich empfängt mich Ihre Gnaden.
(*Er geht nach vorn, die Lakaien zu seiner Linken suchen ihm den Weg zu vertreten.*)
BARON (*zu Octavian mit Interesse*):
Pardon, mein hübsches Kind!
OCTAVIAN (*drecht sich verlegen gegen die Wand*).
BARON (*mit Grazie und Herablassung*):
Ich sag': Pardon, mein hübsches Kind.
MARSCHALLIN (*sieht über die Schulter, steht dann auf und kommt dem Baron entgegen*).
BARON (*galant zu Octavian*):
Ich hab' Ihr doch nicht ernstlich weh getan?
LAKAIEN (*zupfen den Baron, leise*):
Ihre fürstlichen Gnaden!
(*Sie rangieren sich beim Nahen der Marschallin zu einer dichtgeschlossenen Front hart vor der kleinen Türe.*)
BARON (*macht die französische Reverenz mit zwei Wiederholungen*).
MARSCHALLIN: Euer Liebden sehen vortrefflich aus.
BARON (*verneigt sich nochmals, dann zu den Lakaien*):
Sieht Er jetzt wohl, dass Ihre Gnaden entzückt ist, mich
zu sehn.
(*Auf die Marschallin zu, mit weltmännischer Leichtigkeit, indem er ihr die Hand reicht und sie vorführt.*)
Und wie sollten Euer Gnaden nicht!
Was tut die frühe Stunde unter Personen von Stand?
Hab' ich nicht seinerzeit wahrhaftig Tag für Tag
unserer Fürstin Brioche meine Aufwartung gemacht,
da sie im Bad gesessen ist,
mit nichts als einem kleinen Wandschirm zwischen ihr
und mir.
Ich muss mich wundern,
(*zornig umschauend*)
Wenn Euer Gnaden Livree—
OCTAVIAN (*wäre währenddessen gern hinausgeschlüpft; die befremdeten Blicke und Gesichter der Lakaien nötigen ihn zur äussersten Vorsicht, und er zieht sich mit gespielter Unbefangenheit an der Wand gegen dem Alkoven hin zurück*).
MARSCHALLIN: Verzeihen Sie!
Man hat sich betragen, wie es befohlen war.
Ich hatte diesen Morgen die Migräne.
(*Auf einen Wink der Marschallin haben die Lakaien die beiden kleinen Sofas mehr nach vorn gebracht und sind abgegangen.*)
BARON (*sieht öfters nach rückwärts*).
OCTAVIAN (*macht sich möglichst unsichtbar beim Bett zu schaffen*).
MARSCHALLIN (*setzt sich auf das Sofa rechts, nachdem sie dem Baron den Platz auf dem Sofa links angeboten hat*).
BARON (*versucht sich zu setzen, äusserst okkupiert von der Anwesenheit der hübschen Kammerzofe. Für sich*):
Ein hübsches Ding! Ein gutes saub'res Kinderl!

BARON (*pompously to the footmen*) :
Why, never doubt her Highness will receive me.
(*To Octavian, who in confusion turns his face to the wall.*)
Forgive, my pretty child.
(*With gracious condescending.*)
I said, forgive, my pretty child.
(*The Princess looks over her shoulder, rises and goes to meet the Baron.*)

BARON (*gallantly to Octavian*) :
I hope I did not incommode you much.

THE FOOTMEN (*nudging the Baron*) :
Yonder, Sir, is her Highness.
(*The Baron makes an obeisance in the French manner and repeats it twice.*)

PRINCESS : Faith, my dear cousin, you're in looks to-day.

BARON (*to the footmen*) :
Did I not say to you, her Highness would most surely
welcome me?
(*Goes to the Princess with the grace of a man of the world, offers her his hand and leads her to her chair.*)
You will not deny yourself to me?
Of early hours, we of the quality take no account.
Did I not, every morning without fail repair
To the Princess you wot of? Did I not pay my respects
As in her bath she took her ease,
And there was nothing to divide us but a tiny screen?
(*Octavian has made his way along the wall towards the alcove and is busying himself, trying to escape observation, by the bed. In obedience to a sign from the Princess, the footmen carry a little sofa and an armchair to the front and retire.*)
Indeed I wonder
(*Looking around angrily.*)
that any lackey should have dared.

PRINCESS : Forgive them, Coz.
They did but obey me—for 'twas I that bade them,
(*Seats herself on the sofa, after offering the Baron the armchair.*)
I suffered much this morning from the vapours.
(*The Baron tries to sit and is much distracted by the presence of the pretty waiting maid.*)

BARON (*to himself*) :
A pretty wench, egad! She's vastly pleasing.

17

MARSCHALLIN (*aufstehend, ihm zeremoniös aufs neue seinen Platz anbietend*).

BARON (*setzt sich zögernd und bemüht sich, der hübschen Zofe nicht völlig den Rücken zu kehren. Im folgenden wendet er sich bald nach der Marschallin, also nach seiner Linken, bald nach Octavian, also nach seiner Rechten*).

MARSCHALLIN: Ich bin auch jetzt noch nicht ganz wohl.
Der Vetter wird darum vielleicht die Gnade haben—

BARON: Natürlich.
(*Er dreht sich nach seiner Rechten um, um Octavian zu sehen.*)

MARSCHALLIN: Meine Kammerzofe, ein junges Ding vom Land.
Ich muss fürchten, sie inkommodiert Euer Liebden.

BARON (*nach seiner Rechten*):
Ganz allerliebst!
(*Nach seiner Linken.*)
Wie? Nicht im geringsten! Mich? Im Gegenteil!
(*Er winkt Octavian mit der Hand, dann zur Marschallin.*)
Euer Gnaden werden vielleicht verwundert sein, dass ich
als Bräutigam.
(*sieht sich nach seiner Linken um.*)
indes—inzwischen—

MARSCHALLIN: Als Bräutigam?

BARON (*nach seiner Linken*):
Ja, wie Euer Gnaden denn doch wohl aus meinem Brief
genugsam—
(*Nach seiner Rechten.*)
Ein Grasaff', appetitlich, keine fünfzehn Jahr!

MARSCHALLIN (*erleichtert*):
Der Brief, natürlich, ja, der Brief, wer ist denn nur die
Glückliche?
Ich hab' den Namen auf der Zunge.

BARON (*nach seiner Linken*):
Wie?
(*Nach rückwärts.*)
Pudeljung! Gesund! Gewaschen! Allerliebst!

MARSCHALLIN: Wer ist nur schnell die Braut!?

BARON: Das Fräulein Faninal. Ich habe Euer Gnaden den
Namen nicht verheimlicht.

MARSCHALLIN: Natürlich! Wo hab' ich meinen Kopf?
Bloss die Famili ist mir nicht bekannt. Sind's keine
Hiesigen?

OCTAVIAN (*macht sich mit dem Servierbrett zu tun, wodurch er mehr hinter den Rücken des Barons kommt*).

BARON: Jawohl, Euer Gnaden, es sind Hiesige.
Ein durch die Gnade Ihrer Majestät Geadelter.
Er hat die Lieferung für die Armee, die in den Niederlanden steht.

MARSCHALLIN (*bedeutet Octavian ungeduldig mit den Augen, er solle sich fortmachen*).

18

PRINCESS: (*rising and again ceremoniously offering a seat to the Baron*):
    And even now I'm not quite well.

(*The Baron takes his seat with hesitation and tries his utmost not to turn his back to the pretty waiting maid.*)
    And so, dear Cousin,
    Bear me no ill will that I do deny myself . . .

BARON: Nay, truly . . .
                   (*He turns round, so as to look at Octavian.*)

PRINCESS: My own waiting-woman . . . come freshly from the
                             country,
    And I fear that her untaught ways cause you displeasure.

BARON: Charming, I vow . . . Displeasure? Do not think it,
                        I like such ways.

(*Makes a sign to Octavian, then says to the Princess*):
    But your Highness may have felt surprise to learn that I
                    design to take a wife.
                       (*Turns round.*)
    But yet, the reason . . .

PRINCESS: To take a wife?

BARON: As your Highness knows without a doubt, for in my
                    recent letter . . .
    A novice . . . how enticing—barely fifteen years!

PRINCESS (*relieved*):
    You wrote, why surely . . . And who has been so
                       fortunate?
    The name was on my tongue this instant.

BARON: How? And how fresh! egad! how dainty! What a
                       waist!

PRINCESS: Pray tell me who's the bride?

BARON: Young Mistress Faninal.
                  (*With slight vexation.*)
    Yet of her name and station I did make no secret.

PRINCESS: Forgive, I beg, my mem'ry plays me false. What of her
               family, pray, is it native here?

(*Octavian busies himself with the tray and gradually tries to get behind the baron.*)

BARON: Indeed, your Highness, it is native here—
    One which Her Majesty of late has raised to the nobility.
    The whole provisioning of the armies in the Netherlands
                  is in his hands.

(*The Princess impatiently makes signs to Octavian that he should withdraw.*)

BARON (*missversteht ihre Miene durchaus*):
  Ich seh', Euer Gnaden runzeln Dero schöne Stirn ob der
        Mesalliance.
  Allein dass ich sag', das Mädchen ist für einen Engel
        hübsch genug.
  Kommt frischweg aus dem Kloster. Ist das einzige Kind.
          (*Stärker.*)
  Dem Mann gehören zwölf Häuser auf der Wied'n nebst
       dem Palais am Hof.
  Und seine Gesundheit
          (*schmunzelnd*)
  soll nicht die beste sein.
MARSCHALLIN: Mein lieber Vetter, ich kapier' schon, wieviel's gesch-
       lagen hat.
    (*Winkt Octavian, den Rückzug zu nehmen.*)
OCTAVIAN (*will mit dem Servierbrett rückwärts zur Tür hin*).
BARON: Warum hinaus die Schokolade? Geruhen nur! Da!
       Pst, wieso denn!
OCTAVIAN (*steht unschlüssig, das Gesicht abgewendet*):
MARSCHALLIN: Fort, geh' Sie nur!
BARON: Wenn ich Euer Gnaden gesteh',
  dass ich noch so gut wie nüchtern bin.
MARSCHALLIN (*resigniert*):
  Mariandel, komm' Sie her. Servier' Sie Seiner Liebden.
OCTAVIAN (*kommt, serviert an der Rechten des Barons, so dass dieser
  sich wieder zwischen der Marschallin und Octavian befindet.*)
BARON (*nimmt eine Tasse, bedient sich*):
  So gut wie nüchtern, Euer Gnaden. Sitz' im Reisewagen
       seit fünf Uhr früh.
  Recht ein gestelltes Ding!
        (*Zu Octavian.*)
  Bleib' Sie dahier, mein Herz.
  Ich hab' Ihr was zu sagen.
       (*Zur Marschallin, laut.*)
  Meine ganze Livree, Stallpagen, Jäger, alles—
         (*Er frisst.*)
  Alles unten im Hof zusamt meinen Almosenier.
MARSCHALLIN (*zu Octavian*):
  Geh' Sie nur.
BARON (*zu Octavian*):
  Hat Sie noch ein Biskoterl? Bleib' Sie doch!
         (*Leise.*)
  Sie ist ein süsser Engelsschatz, ein saubrer.
       (*Zur Marschallin.*)
  Sind auf dem Wege zum "Weissen Ross", wo wir logieren,
       heisst bis übermorgen—
       (*Halblaut zu Octavian.*)
  Ich gäb' was Schönes drum, mit Ihr—
       (*zur Marschallin, sehr laut.*)
  bis übermorgen—
       (*schnell zu Octavian.*)
  unter vier Augen zu scharmutzieren! Wie?

I see your Highness' pretty lips express disdain at such a
misalliance.
But then, although I say it, the girl is pretty as an angel
and as good,
Comes straight from out a convent, is an only child.
The man has half a score of houses in the city and has a
mansion too.
His health too is failing

(*Chuckles.*)

so the physicians say.

PRINCESS: It needs no glasses to discover what hour of day it is.

(*Repeats her signs to Octavian to retire.*)
(*Octavian tries to back to the door with the tray.*)

BARON: Why leave the chocolate unfinished?
(*To Octavian, who stands undecided with averted face.*)
Hey! Pst! Pst! What ails you?

PRINCESS: Quick, get you gone!

BARON: Grant me permision, your Highness,
To say that I am faint for food.

PRINCESS (*resigned*):
Mariandel, bring it back and wait upon his Lordship.

BARON: As good as fasting, my dear cousin—sitting in my post-
chaise since the early dawn

(*Octavian brings the tray to the Baron, who takes a cup and fills it.*)
Gad, what a strapping wench!

(*To Octavian.*)

Do not go yet, my child,
There's something I would tell you.

(*To the Princess.*)

All my suite I have brought—footmen and grooms and
couriers—
They are all down below together with my almoner.

PRINCESS (*to Octavian*):
You may go.

BARON (*to Octavian*):
Have you another biscuit?   Do not go—
It is the daintiest morsel, sweet and adorable.

(*To the Princess.*)

I halted here, but we are lodging at an inn, the White
Horse,

(*Softly to Octavian.*)

I'd pay a heavy price to court you. . . .

(*To the Princess, very loud.*)

But till to-morrow.

(*To Octavian.*)

When there is no one by to mar our pleasure.

21

MARSCHALLIN (*muss lachen über Octavians freches Komödienspiel.*)

BARON: Dann ziehn wir ins Palais von Faninal.
Natürlich muss ich vorher den Bräutigamsaufführer —
(*wütend zu Octavian.*)
will Sie denn nicht warten? —
an die wohlgeborne Jungfer Braut deputieren,
Der die silberne Rosen überbringt
nach der hochadeligen Gepflogenheit.

MARSCHALLIN: Und wen von der Verwandtschaft haben Euer Liebden
für dieses Ehrenamt ausersehn?
wen denn nur?
den Vetter Jörger? Wie? Den Vetter Lamberg?
Ich werde —

BARON: Dies liegt in Euer Gnaden allerschönsten Händen.

MARSCHALLIN: Ganz gut. Will Er mit mir zu Abend essen, Vetter?
Sagen wir morgen, will Er? Dann proponier' ich Ihm
einen.

BARON: Euer Gnaden sind die Herablassung selber.

MARSCHALLIN (*will aufstehen*):
Indes —

BARON (*halblaut*):
Das Sie mir wiederkommt! Ich geh' nicht eher fort!

MARSCHALLIN (*für sich*):
Oho!
(*Laut.*)
Bleib' Sie nur da! Kann ich dem Vetter
für jetzt noch dienlich sein?

BARON: Ich shäme mich bereits:
An Euer Gnaden Notari eine Rekommandation
wär mir lieb.
Es handelt sich um den Eh'vertrag.

MARSCHALLIN: Mein Notari kommt öfters des Morgens. Schau' Sie
doch, Mariandel,
ob er nicht in der Antichambre ist und wartet.

BARON: Wozu das Kammerzofel?
Euer Gnaden beraubt sich der Bedienung
um meinetwillen.
(*Hält zie auf.*)

MARSCHALLIN: Lass Er doch, Vetter, Sie mag ruhig gehn.

BARON (*lebhaft*):
Das geb' ich nicht zu, bleib' Sie dahier zu Ihrer Gnaden
Wink.
Es kommt gleich wer von der Livree herein.
Ich liess ein solches Goldkind, meiner Seel',
nicht unter das infame Lakaienvolk.

MARSCHALLIN: Euer Liebden sind allzu besorgt.

HAUSHOFMEISTER (*tritt ein*).

(The Princess cannot refrain from laughing at Octavian's impudent by-play.)

Then I and mine will be the guest of Faninal.
But first, I must despatch the bridegroom's Ambassador,

(Angrily to Octavian.)

Will you not have patience?
To my highly-born and beauteous bride, one who shall
bring to her
As a pledge of love a silver Rose,
As in all noble families the custom is.

PRINCESS: On whom of all our kinsmen has your Lordship's choice
Fallen for this grave Embassy?
Who is fit? Our cousin Preysing? Or Kinsman Lambert...
I'll tell you...

BARON: All this I gladly leave in your sweet hands, your Highness.

PRINCESS: 'Tis well. Will you not sup with me to-night, dear kinsman?
Or else to-morrow? I'll not fail then with proposals.

BARON: Nay, your Highness' condescension overwhelms me.

PRINCESS *(rising)*:
But yet . . .

BARON *(aside)*:
You must come back again. I stay till you are here!

PRINCESS *(aside)*:
Oho!

(To Octavian.)

Stay where you are. Will you command me
For aught, dear Cousin, now?

BARON: Nay, truly, I'm ashamed . . .
A word or two to commend me to your Highness's at-
torney
I would crave.
A conference, touching settlements.

PRINCESS: My man of law is often here thus early.
Go to seek Mariandel,

(To Octavian.)

If he's by chance yet in the anteroom in waiting.

BARON: Why send your waiting-woman?
Her help your Highness might be needing—
'Tis too much kindness.

(Holds Octavian back.)

PRINCESS: Let her be, Cousin, she's not needed here.

BARON *(eagerly)*:
That will I not allow.

(To Octavian.)

Stay you here, at her Highness's beck and call,
'Twill not be long before a footman comes.
I should not let this sweet child, on my soul,
Go mix with all the scurvy men below.

(Stroking Octavian's hands.)

PRINCESS: There's no need for such fear, my dear Coz.

(Enter the Major-Domo.)

23

BARON: Da, hab' ich's nicht gesagt?
Er wird Euer Gnaden zu melden haben.

MARSCHALLIN (*zum Haushofmeister*):
Struhan, hab' ich meinen Notari in der Vorkammer
warten?

HAUSHOFMEISTER: Fürstliche Gnaden haben den Notari,
dann den Verwalter, dann den Kuchelchef,
dann von Excellenz Silva hegeschickt
ein Sänger mit einem Flötisten.

(*Trocken.*)
Ansonsten das gewöhnliche Bagagi.

BARON (*hat sein Sofa hinter den breiten Rücken des Haushofmeisters
geschoben, ergreift zärtlich die Hand der vermeintlichen Zofe*):
Hat sie schon einmal
mit einem Kavalier im tête-à-tête
zu Abend g'essen?

OCTAVIAN (*tut sehr verlegen*).

BARON: Nein? Da wird Sie Augen machen. Will Sie?

OCTAVIAN (*leise, verschämt*):
I weiss halt nit, i dös derf.

MARSCHALLIN (*dem Haushofmeister unaufmerksam zuhörend, beobachtet
die beiden, muss leise lachen*).

HAUSHOFMEISTER (*verneigt sich, tritt zurück, wodurch die Gruppe für
den Blick der Marschallin frei wird*).

MARSCHALLIN (*lachend zum Haushofmeister*):
Warten lassen.

(*Haushofmeister ab.*)
BARON (*setzt sich möglichst unbefangen zurecht und nimmt eine gravi-
tätische Miene an*).

MARSCHALLIN (*lachend*):
Der Vetter ist, ich seh', kein Kostverächter.

BARON (*erleichtert*):
Mit Euer Gnaden

(*aufatmend*)
ist man frei daran. Da gibt's keine Flausen, keine
Etikette,
keine spanische Tuerei!

(*Er küsst der Marschallin die Hand.*)
MARSCHALLIN (*amusiert*):
Aber wo Er doch ein Bräutgam ist?

BARON (*halb aufstehend, ihr genähert*):
Macht das einen lahmen Esel aus mir?
Bin ich da nicht wie ein guter Hund auf einer guten
Fährte?
Und doppelt scharf auf jedes Wild: nach links nach
rechts?

MARSCHALLIN: Ich seh', Euer Liebden betreiben es als Profession.

24

BARON :   There, is it not as I said?
                  He comes with some news that concerns your Highness.

PRINCESS :   Struban, tell me, is my attorney waiting in the ante-
                                                                chamber?

MAJOR-DOMO : Yes, the attorney waits without, your Highness,
                  Then there's the Steward, next the Head Cook—
                  Then, the Duke of Silva commends
                  To your Highness a singer and a flute-player,

                                                                (Drily.)
                  And lastly all the usual petitioners.

BARON *(to Octavian)* :

                  Say, have you ever, with any gentleman
                  Been tête-à-tête to supper, Mariandel?

                                      (Octavian simulates embarrassment.)
                  No? It will make you stare, I warrant.

OCTAVIAN *(softly, confused)* :
                  Her Highness won't let me, I'm sure.

            *(The Princess listens inattentively to the Major-Domo, while watching
            the Baron and Octavian with much amusement.)*

PRINCESS *(to the Major-Domo)* :
                  Let them wait then.

                                              (Exit Major-Domo.)
                      (To the Baron, who tries to regain his composure.)
                  My cousin takes, I notice, pleasure where he finds it.

BARON *(relieved)* :

                  Your Highness puts me at my ease at once.
                  With you we have no nonsense and no Spanish affectations.

                                              (Kissing her hand.)
                  No airs, no buckram, and no compliments.

PRINCESS *(amused)* :
                  But a man of birth, who's just betrothed . . .

BARON *(approaching her)* :
                  Must I, because of that, live like a monk?
                  Do I not well, like a hound of breed, keen on the quarry
                                                                ever.
                  To follow hot-foot every scent to right or left?

PRINCESS :   I see now that my cousin pursues his sport quite seriously.

25

BARON :   Das will ich meinen.
              Wüsste nicht, welche mir besser behagen könnte.
              Ich muss Euer Gnaden sehr bedauern,
              dass Euer Gnaden nur — wie drück' ich mich aus —
              die verteidigenden Erfahrungen besitzen.
              Parole d'honneur! Es geht nichts über die von der
                                                anderen Seite.

MARSCHALLIN *(lacht)* :
              Ich glaube Ihm, dass die sehr mannigfaltig sind.

BARON :   Soviel Zeiten das Jahr, soviel Stunden der Tag, da ist
                                                keine —-

MARSCHALLIN : Keine?

BARON :   Wo nicht —

MARSCHALLIN : Wo nicht —

BARON :   Wo nicht dem Knaben Cupido
              ein Geschenkerl abzulisten wär'!

BARON *(lässt von Octavian ab und nimmt wieder würdevolle Haltung an)* :
              Geben mir Euer Gnaben den Grasaff' da
              zu meiner künftigen Frau Gemahlin Bedienung.

MARSCHALLIN : Wie, meine Kleine da? Was sollte die?
              Die Fräulein Braut wird schon versehen sein
              und nicht anstehn auf Euer Liebden Auswahl.

BARON :   Das ist ein feines Ding! Kreuzsakerlot!
              Da ist ein Tropfen guten Bluts dabei!

OCTAVIAN *(für sich)* :
              Ein Tropfen guten Bluts!

MARSCHALLIN : Euer Liebden haben ein scharfes Auge!

BARON :   Geziemt sich.
                                                (Vertraulich.)
              Find' in der Ordnung, dass Personen von Stand
              in solcher Weise von adeligem Blut bedient werden.
              Führ' selbst ein Kind meiner Laune mit mir.

OCTAVIAN :   Ein Kind Seiner Laune?

MARSCHALLIN : Wie? Gar ein Mädel? Das will ich nicht hoffen.

BARON :   Nein, einen Sohn. Trägt lerchenauisches Gepräge im
                                                Gesicht.
              Halt' ihn als Leiblakai.
              Wenn Euer Gnaden dann werden befehlen,
              dass ich die silberne Rosen darf Dero Händen übergeben,
              wird er es sein, der sie herauf bringt.

MARSCHALLIN : Soll mich recht freuen. Aber wart' Er einmal.
                                                (Octavian winkend.)
BARON :   Geben mir Euer Gnaden das Zofel! Ich lass nicht locker.

MARSCHALLIN : Ei! Geh' Sie und bring' Sie das Medaillon her.

OCTAVIAN *(leise)* :
              Theres! Theres, gib acht!

MARSCHALLIN *(ebenso)* :
              Bring's nur schnell! Ich weiss schon, was ich tu.

                                26

BARON: And why deny it?
For what sport more becomes a man of birth and breeding?
I vow, I do condole with you sincerely
That you can only know—'tis hard to express—
From experience the sensations of defenders—
Parole d'honneur—nothing can equal those which inspire
                     the attacking party.

PRINCESS: I doubt not they are vastly various.

BARON: Though the months of the year, though the hours and the
                     minutes be many . . .

PRINCESS: Many?

BARON: There's none . . .

PRINCESS: There's none?

BARON: In which sly Master Cupido
Will not smile upon him who woos him aright.

BARON (*suddenly resumes his dignified bearing*):
Pray will your Highness permit me to take this wench
To be my Baroness's chosen attendant!

PRINCESS: What, my favorite girl? What could you gain?
And sure, your bride will have no need of her,
Such a choice she would wish to make unaided.

BARON: That is a splendid wench, Gadzooks, she is!
I dare be sworn, she has blue blood in her.

OCTAVIAN (*aside*):
Yes, blue blood indeed.

PRINCESS: What a keen discernment is yours, my cousin.

BARON: 'Tis needful.
                           (*Confidentially.*)

Is it not right, that a man of birth
Should have those about his person
Who also are of pedigree unblemished?
I have a lackey as well-born as I.

OCTAVIAN (*still much amused*):
As well-born as he is!

PRINCESS: What? I am curious. How vastly diverting!

BARON: Son of a Prince . . .

PRINCESS and OCTAVIAN: Of a Prince?

BARON: So like, that none can mistake him, are the two.
He is my body-servant.

PRINCESS and OCTAVIAN (*laughing*):
His body-servant!

BARON: Whenever your Highness shall deign to command me
To give to your keeping the Rose of Silver
(He is without now—in the courtyard)
'Twill be from him I shall receive it.

PRINCESS: I understand—but one instant, I beg,
                  (*Beckoning to Octavian.*)
Mariandel!

BARON: Once more I beg your Highness—the waiting maid for My
                           Lady!

PRINCESS: Ah!
                        (*To Octavian.*)
Go bring the miniature set in jewels . . .

OCTAVIAN (*softly*):
Thérèse, Thérèse, beware!

PRINCESS: Bring it quick! I am caution itself, never fear.
                          (*Exit Octavian.*)

BARON (*Octavian nachsehend*) :
　　Könnt' eine junge Fürstin sein.
　　　　　　　　(*Dann, im Konversationston.*)
　　Hab' vor, meiner Braut eine getreue Kopie
　　meines Stammbaumes zu spendieren —
　　nebst einer Locke vom Ahnherrn Lerchenau, der ein
　　　　　　　　grosser Klosterstifter war
　　und Oberst-Erblandhofmeister in Kärnten
　　und in der winischen Mark.

OCTAVIAN (*bringt das Medaillon aus dem Bettalkoven*).

MARSCHALLIN : Wollen Euer Gnaden leicht den jungen Herrn da als
　　Bräutigamsaufführer haben?

BARON : 　　Bin ungeschauter einverstanden!

MARSCHALLIN (*etwas zögernd*) :
　　Mein junger Vetter, der Graf Octavian.

BARON : 　　Wüsste keinen vornehmeren zu wünschen!
　　Wär in Devotion dem jungen Herrn sehr verbunden!

MARSCHALLIN (*schnell*) :
　　Seh' Er ihn an!
　　　　　　　　(*Hält ihm das Medaillon hin.*)

BARON (*sieht bald auf das Medaillon, bald auf die Zofe*) :
　　Die Aehnlichkeit!

MARSCHALLIN : Ja, ja.

BARON : 　　Aus dem Gesicht geschnitten!

MARSCHALLIN : Hab' mir auch schon Gedanken gemacht.
　　　　　　　　(*Auf das Medaillon deutend.*)
　　Rofrano, des Herrn Marchese zweiter Bruder.

BARON : 　　Octavian Rofrano! Da ist man wer, wenn man aus
　　　　　　　　solchem Haus,
　　　　　　　　(*mit Beziehung auf die Zofe.*)
　　Und wär's auch bei der Domestikentür!

MARSCHALLIN : Darum halt' ich sie auch wie was Besonderes.

BARON : 　　Geziemt sich.

MARSCHALLIN : Immer um meine Person.

BARON : 　　Sehr wohl.

MARSCHALLIN : Jetzt aber geh' Sie, Mariandel, mach' Sie fort.

BARON : 　　Wie denn? Sit kommt doch wieder.

MARSCHALLIN (*überhört den Baron absichtlich*) :
　　Und lass Sie die Antichambre herein.

OCTAVIAN (*geht gegen die Flügelthür rechts*).

BARON (*ihm nach*) :
　　Mein schönstes Kind!

OCTAVIAN (*an der Tür rechts*) :
　　Derft's eina geh'!
　　　　　　　　(*Läuft nach der andern Tür.*)

BARON (*ihm nach*) :
　　Ich bin Ihr Serviteur! Geb' Sie doch einen Augenblick
　　　　　　　　Audienz!

BARON (*looking after him*):
>Gad, she might be a young Princess.
>
>>(*To the Princess.*)
>
>Think you it would be well if to my bride I gave
>My pedigree, fairly copied—
>Or e'en a lock of the first of the Lerchenaus—a pious
>>founder of convents he
>And First Hereditary Grand Warden
>of the Karinthian Domains?
>
>>(*Octavian brings the medalion.*)

PRINCESS:
>Would your Lordship choose to have this gentleman
>To take the Rose of Silver to your mistress?
>
>>(*All in an easy tone of conversation.*)

BARON:
>Without a glance I trust your Highness.

PRINCESS (*hesitating*):
>'Tis my young cousin, Count Octavian—

BARON (*still very courteous*):
>Who could wish for a nobler or more gallant?
>And vastly to your kinsman should I be indebted.

PRINCESS (*quickly*):
>Look at him well.
>
>>(*Shows him the miniature.*)

BARON:
>'Tis wonderful.
>
>>(*Looking first at the portrait, then at Octavian.*)
>
>Like two copies from one model!

PRINCESS:
>It has caused me myself no small surprise.
>
>>(*Pointing to the portrait.*)
>
>Rofrano, the younger brother of the Marquis.

BARON:
>Octavian? Rofrano? 'Tis no small thing, such a relation-
>>ship,
>
>>(*Pointing to Octavian.*)
>
>E'en if it be not quite . . . canonical.

PRINCESS:
>For that same cause have I advanced her over all the rest.

BARON:
>'Tis fitting—

PRINCESS:
>Always in waiting on myself.

BARON:
>'Tis well.

PRINCESS:
>Now get you gone, you, Mariandel.
>
>>(*Octavian goes towards the folding door on the right.*)

BARON (*following him*):
>My sweetest child!

OCTAVIAN:
>La! Naughty man!
>
>>(*At the door.*)

BARON:
>I am your most obedient servant—Only let me speak.

29

OCTAVIAN: (*schlägt ihm die kleine Tür vor der Nase zu*):
I komm' glei.

(*In diesem Augenblick tritt eine alte Kammerfrau, die Waschbecken, Kanne und Handtuch trägt, durch die gleiche Türe ein. Der Baron zieht sich enttäuscht zurück. Zwei Lakaien kommen von rechts herein, bringen einen Wandschirm aus dem Alkoven, die alte Kammerfrau, mit ihr, zwei Lakaien tragen den Sessel und den Frisiertisch nach vorne in die Mitte. Zwei Lakaien öffnen die Flügeltüren rechts. Es treten ein der Notar, der Küchenchef, hinter diesen ein Küchenjunge, der das Menübuch trägt. Dann die Modistin, ein Gelehrter mit einem Folianten und der Tierhändler mit winzig kleinen Hunden und einen Aeffchen. Valzacchi und Annina, hinter diesen rasch gleitend, nehmen den vordersten Platz links ein, die adelige Mutter mit ihren drei Töchtern, alle in Trauer, stellen sich in den rechten Flügel. Der Haushofmeister führt den Tenor und den Flötisten nach vorne. Baron rückwärts winkt einen Lakaien zu sich, gibt ihm den Auftrag, zeigt: „Hier durch die Hintertür".*)

DIE DREI ADELIGEN TÖCHTER (*schreiend*):
Drei arme adelige Waisen —

DIE ADELIGE MUTTER (*bedeutet ihnen, nicht so zu schreien und niederzuknien*).

DIE DREI WAISEN (*niederkniend*):   •
Drei arme adelige Waisen
erflehen Dero hohen Schutz!

MODISTIN (*laut*):
Le chapeau Paméla! La poudre à la reine de Golconde!

DER TIERHÄNDLER: Schöne Affen, wenn Durchlaucht schaffen,
auch Vögel hab' ich da aus Afrika.

DIE DREI WAISEN: Der Vater ist jung auf dem Felde der Ehre gefallen,
ihm dieses nachzutun, ist unser Herzensziel.

MODISTIN: La chapeau Paméla! C'est la merveille du monde!

DER TIERHÄNDLER: Papageien hätt' ich da,
aus Indien und Afrika.
Hunderln, so klein
und schon zimmerrein.

(*Marschallin tritt hervor, alles verneigt sich. Baron ist links vorgekommen.*)

MARSCHALLIN (*zum Baron*):
Ich präsentier' Euer Liebden hier den Notar.

(*Notar tritt mit Verneigung gegen den Frisiertisch, wo sich die Marschallin niedergelassen, zum Baron links. Marschallin winkt die jüngste der drei Waisen zu sich, lässt sich vom Haushofmeister einen Geldbeutel reichen, gibt ihn dem Mädchen, indem sie es auf die Stirne küsst. Gelehrter will vortreten, seine Folianten überreichen, Valzacchi springt vor, drängt ihn zur Seite.*)

OCTAVIAN (*slams the door in the Baron's face*):
> Yes, shortly.

(*At this moment an old tirewoman enters by the same door. The Baron starts back disappointed. Two Footmen enter from the right and bring a screen from the recess. The Princess steps behind the screen, attended by her tirewoman. The toilet table is moved to the centre. The footmen open the folding doors through which enter the Attorney, the Head Cook, followed by an assistant, carrying the book of Menus. Then a Milliner, a Scholar, carrying a ponderous folio, and the Vendor of Animals with tiny lap-dogs and a small monkey. Valzacchi and Annina slipping in behind the last-named, take their places on the extreme left. The noble Mother with her three Daughters all in deepest mourning take position on the right wing. The Major-Domo leads the Tenor and the Flute Player to the front. The Baron, in the background beckons to a footman, gives him an order, pointing "Here through the small door."*)

THE THREE NOBLE ORPHANS (*shrilly*):
> Three poor and high-born orphan children . . .

(*Their Mother makes signs to them to kneel and not to sing so loudly.*)

THE THREE ORPHANS (*kneeling*):
> Three poor and highborn orphan children,
> Implore your Grace to grant our prayer.

THE MILLINER (*loudly*):
> Le Chapeau Pamèla—La Poudre à la Reine de Golconda!

THE VENDOR OF ANIMALS: For your pleasure
> In hours of leisure
> Of tricksy apes a score
> From Afric's shore.

THE THREE ORPHANS: My father in youth died a glorious death for his
> country,
> 'Tis my heart's one desire to be his worthy child.

THE MILLINER: Le Chapeau Pamèla! C'est la merveille du monde!

THE VENDOR: Parrots too of plumage gay
> From India and Africay.
> Lap-dogs so wise
> Very small in size.

(*The Princess appears. All bow low. The Baron, on the left, steps forward.*)

PRINCESS (*to the Baron*):
> I here make known to you, dear Kinsman, my attorney.

(*The Attorney, with many obeisances towards the toilet table at which the Princess has seated herself, advances to the Baron on the right. The Princess signs to the youngest of the three Orphans to approach her, and takes a purse from the Major-Domo and gives it to the girl, whom she kisses on the forehead. The Scholar attempts to approach the Princess and hand her his volumes, but Valzacchi rushes forward and pushes him aside.*)

31

VALZACCHI (*ein schwarzgerändertes Zeitungsblatt hervorziehend*):
Die swarze Seitung! Fürstlike Gnade:
Alles 'ier ge'eim gesrieben!
Nur für 'ohe Persönlikeite.
Die swarze Seitung!
Eine Leikname in 'Interkammer
von eine gräflike Palais!
Eine Bürgersfrau mit der amante
vergiften der Hehemann
diese Nackt um dreie Huhr!

MARSCHALLIN: Lass er mich mit dem Tratsch in Ruh'!

VALZACCHI: In Gnaden:
Tutte quante Vertraulikeite
aus die grosse Welt!

MARSCHALLIN: Ich will nix wissen! Lass er mich mit dem Tratsch in
Ruh'!

VALZACCHI (*mit bedauernder Verbeugung springt zurück*).

DIE DREI WAISEN (*zuletzt auch die Mutter, haben der Marschallin die
Hand geküsst*):
Glück und Segen allerwegen Euer Gnaden hohem Sinn!
Eingegraben steht erhaben er in unsern Herzen drin.
(*Gehen ab samt der Mutter.*)

(*Der Friseur tritt hastig auf, der Gehilfe stürzt ihm mit fliegenden
Rockschössen nach. Der Friseur fasst die Marschallin ins Auge
verdüstert sich, tritt zurück, er studiert ihr heutiges Aussehen.
Der Gehilft indessen packt aus am Frisiertisch. Der Friseur
schiebt einige Personen zurück, sich Spielraum zu schaffen. Nach
einer kurzen Ueberlegung ist sein Plan gefasst, er eilt mit Ent-
schlossenheit auf die Marschallin zu, beginnt zu frisieren. Ein
Läuffer in rosa, schwarz und Silber tritt auf, überbringt ein Billet.
Haushofmeister mit Silbertablett ist schnell zur Hand, präsentiert es der Marschallin. Friseur hält inne, sie lesen zu lassen.
Gehilfe reicht ihm ein neues Eisen. Friseur schwenkt es: ist
zu heiss. Gehilfe reicht ihm nach fragendem Blick auf die Marschallin das Billet, die nickt, worauf er es lächelnd verwendet,
um das Eisen zu kühlen. Gleichzeitig hat sich der Sänger in
Position gestellt, hält das Notenblatt. Flötist sieht ihm, begleitend,
über die Schultern. Die Lakaien haben rechts ganz vorne Stellung genommen, andere stehen im Hintergrund.*)

DER TENOR: Di rigori armato il seno
Contro amor mi ribellai
Ma fui vinto in un baleno
In mirar due vaghi rai.
Ahi! che resiste puoco
Cor di gelo a stral di fuoco.

VALZACCHI (*drawing from his pocket a black-edged news sheet*):
Ze latest scandals! True news, your 'Ighness!
Learnt from secret information!
Meant only for ze Quality!
Ze newest Scandals!
A dead body in a secret chamber
In ze town 'ouse of a Count!
A rich merchant's wife poisons 'er 'usband
Viz ze 'elp of her lover
Soon after sree o'clock zis night.

PRINCESS: Fudge! Let me hear no more of it!

VALZACCHI: Your pardon, your 'Ighness
Tutte quante. Ze hidden secrets
Of ze elegant world!

PRINCESS: What is that to me? Let me be with your vicious talk!

(*Valzacchi retires with a deprecatory bow. The three Orphans prepare to withdraw, after they and their Mother have kissed the Princess's hand.*)

THE THREE ORPHANS (*whining*):
May Heav'n joy send you, may bliss attend you
Wheresoever you may be,
We shall praise ever, forgetting never
Your great generosity!

(*Exeunt with their Mother.*)

(*The Hairdresser hurriedly steps forward, his assistant follows him with flying coat-tails. The Hairdresser gazes at the Princess, looks solemn and steps back a few paces, the better to study her appearance. In the meantime the assistant unpacks his paraphernalia at the toilet table. The Hairdresser pushes several persons back, so as to make more room for himself.*)

The Flute Player now steps forward and begins his Cadenza. Some Footmen have taken up positions at the front to the right. Others remain in the background.

After brief deliberation, the Hairdresser has made up his mind and with an air of determination goes to the Princess and begins to dress her hair. A Courier in a livery of pink, black and silver, enters carrying a note. The Major-Domo is quickly at hand with a silver salver and presents it to the Princess. The Hairdresser pauses to allow her to read. The assistant hands him a fresh pair of curling tongs. The Hairdresser swings it: it is too hot. The assistant gives him, after a questioning glance at the Princess, who nods assent, the note, which he smilingly uses for cooling the tongs. The Singer has taken up his position.)

THE TENOR (*reading from a sheet of music*):
Di rigori armeto il seno
Contro amor mi ribellai
Ma fui vinto in un baleno
In mirar due vaghi rai
Ahi! Che resiste poco
Cor di gelo a stral di fuoco!

(*Der Friseur übergibt dem Gehilfen das Eisen und applaudiert dem Sänger. Dann fährt er im Arrangement des Lockenbaues fort. Ein Bedienter hat indessen bei der kleinen Tür den Kammerdiener des Barons, den Almosenier und den Jäger eingelassen. Es sind drei bedenkliche Gestalten. Der Kammerdiener ist ein junger grosser Lümmel, der dumm und frech aussieht. Er trägt unterm Arm ein Futteral aus rotem Saffian. Der Almosenier ist ein verwildeter Dorfkooperator, ein vier Schuh hoher, aber stark und verwegen aussehender Gnom. Der Leibjäger mag, bevor er in die schlechtsitzende Livree gesteckt wurde, Mist geführt haben. Der Almosenier und der Kammerdiener scheinen sich um den Vortritt zu streiten und steigen einander auf die Füsse. Sie steuern längs der linken Seite auf ihren Herrn zu, in dessen Nähe sie Halt machen.*)*

BARON (*auf dem Faninal links ganz vorne zum Notar, der vor ihm steht, seine Weisungen entgegennimmt. Halblaut*):
Als Morgengabe — ganz separatim jedoch —
und vor der Mitgift — bin ich verstanden, Herr Notar? —
kehrt Schloss und Herrschaft Gaunersdorf an mich zurück!
Von Lasten frei und ungemindert an Privilegien,
so wie mein Vater selig sie besessen hat.

NOTAR (*kurzatmig*):
Gestatten hochfreiherrliche Gnaden die submisseste Belehrung,
dass eine Morgengabe wohl vom Gatten an die Gattin,
nicht aber von der Gattin an den Gatten
(*tief aufatmend.*)
bestellet oder stipuliert zu werden, fähig ist.

BARON: Das mag wohl sein.

NOTAR: Dem ist so —

BARON: Aber im besondern Fall —

NOTAR: Die Formen und die Präskriptionen kennen keinen Unterschied.

BARON (*schreit*):
Haben ihn aber zu kennen:

NOTAR (*erschrocken*):
In Gnaden!

BARON (*wieder leise, aber eindringlich und voll hohen Selbstgefühles*):
Wenn eines hochadeligen Blutes blühender Spross sich herablässt
im Ehebette einer so gut als bürgerlichen Mamsell Faninal
—bin ich verstanden?—acte de présence zu machen
vor Gott und der Welt und sozusagen
angesichts kaiserlicher Majestät —

DER FLÖTIST (*beginnt wieder zu präludieren*).

(The Hairdresser hands the tongs to his assistant and applauds the singer. Then he continues to work at the coiffure of the Princess. In the meantime a Footman has admitted through the small door the Body Servant, the Almoner and the Chasseur of the Baron. They are three strange apparitions. The Body Servant is a tall young fellow of foolish insolent mien. He carries under his arm a leather jewel case. The Almoner is an unkempt village councillor, a stunted but strong and bold-looking imp. The Chasseur looks as if, before being thrust into his ill-fitting livery, he had worked in the farm. The Almoner and the Body Servant seem to be fighting for precedence, and trip each other up. They steer a course to the left, towards their master, in whose vicinity they come to a halt.)

BARON *(seated, to the Attorney, who stands before him, taking his instructions)*:

As compensation, as a separate gift,
Before the dowry, Master Attorney, understand,
I shall receive the title-deeds of Gaunersdorf,
Released from all encumbrances and all claims whatsoever.
With privileges intact, just as my father held them.

ATTORNEY *(asthmatic)*:

Your Lordship — with dutiful submission — has not been
pleased to remember
That a donatio ante nuptias may be given by the husband
But cannot ever come from wife to husband—

(Fetching a deep breath.)
Such contracts are unprecedented quite.

BARON: That may be so.

ATTORNEY: It is so.

BARON: But in this special case—

ATTORNEY: The statutes are precise, no way is known of circumventing
them.

BARON *(shouts)*:

But I insist that you shall know one.

ATTORNEY *(alarmed)*:

Your pardon.

BARON: But, do you see, when a noble race's chief condescends to a
union
With a young person, a Mistress Faninal,
Whose father has no pedigree — upon whose patent of
nobility
The ink is scarcely dry — if then I choose in face of
Heaven
And of the Empress thus to honour her.

(The Flautist begins another Prelude.)

35

BARON: Da wird, corpo di Bacco! von Morgengabe
als geziemendem Geschenk dankbarer Devotion
für die Hingab' so hohen Blutes
sehr wohl die Rede sein!
*(Sänger macht miene wieder anzufangen, wartet noch, bis der Baron
still wird.)*

NOTAR *(zum Baron, leise)*:
Vielleicht, dass man die Sache separatim—

BARON *(leise)*:
Er ist ein schmählicher Pedant: als Morgengabe will ich
das Gütel!

NOTAR *(ebenso)*:
Als einen wohl verklausulierten Teil der Mitgift—

BARON *(halblaut)*:
Als Morgengabe! Geht das nicht in Seinen Schädel!

NOTAR *(ebenso)*:
Als eine Schenkung inter vivos oder—

BARON *(schlägt wütend auf den Tisch, schreiend)*:
Als Morgengabe:

DER SÄNGER *(während des Gesprächs der beiden)*:
Ma si caro è'l mio tormento
Dolce è si la piaga mia,
Ch' il penare è mio contento
E'l sanarmi è tirannia
Ahi! Che resiste puoco—
Cor......

*(Hier erhebt der Baron seine Stimme so, dass der Sänger jäh ab-
bricht, desgleichen die Flöte.)*

NOTAR *(zieht sich erschrocken in die Ecke zurück).*

MARSCHALLIN *(winkt den Sänger zu sich, reicht ihm die Hand zum Kuss).*

SÄNGER NEBST FLÖTIST *(ziehen sich unter tiefen Verbeugungen zurück).*

BARON *(tut, als ob nichts geschehen wäre, winkt dem Sänger leutselig zu,
tritt dann zu seiner Dienerschaft, streicht dem Leiblakai die
bäurisch in die Stirn gekämmten Haare hinaus; geht dann, als
suchte er jemand, zur kleinen Tür, öffnet sie, spioniert hinaus,
ärgert sich, dass die Zofe nicht zurückkommt; schnüffelt gegen's
Bett, schüttelt den Kopf, kommt dann wieder vor).*

MARSCHALLIN *(sieht sich in dem Handspiegel, halblaut)*:
Mein lieber Hippolyte,
Heut haben Sie ein altes Weib aus mir gemacht:
*(Der Friseur mit Bestürzung wirft sich fieberhaft auf den Locken-
bau der Marschallin und verändert ihn aufs neue. Das Gesicht der
Marschallin bleibt traurig.)*

MARSCHALLIN *(über die Schulter zum Haushofmeister)*:
Abtreten die Leut'!

I think, corpo di Bacco, that such is clearly
A case where an exception can be made, and that the bride
Should have full leave to show her gratitude
For the honour done to her.

ATTORNEY (*to the Baron, softly*):
Perhaps by means of purchase and conveyance . . .

BARON (*to himself*):
The wretched pettifogging fool!   As compensation I must
have it!

ATTORNEY: Or in the marriage settlement, with special clauses . . .

BARON: No—compensation. Can you not get that into your thick
skull?

ATTORNEY: Or as donatio inter vivos—or else.

BARON (*in a fury, thumping the table, shouts*):
No, compensation.

THE TENOR (*during this conversation*):
Ma si caro è il mio tormento
Dolce è si la piaga mia,
Che il penare è mio contento
E'l sanarmi è tirannia
Ahi che resiste poco
Cor . . . . .

(*At this point the Baron raises his voice so that the Singer ends
abruptly, likewise the Flute Player.*)

(*The Princess beckons the Singer and gives him her hand to kiss.
The Singer and the Flute Player retire with deep obeisances. The
Attorney withdraws into a corner in alarm. The Baron does
as if nothing had happened, and makes a sign of condescending
approval to the Singer, then goes across to his servants; straightens
the towzled hair of his body servant; then goes, as if looking for
somebody, to the small door, opens it, peers out, is annoyed, looks
by the bed, shakes his head and comes forward again.*)

PRINCESS (*looking at herself in a hand mirror, aside*):
My good friend Hippolyte, this will not do,
You've made me look a very fright.

(*The Hairdresser in consternation falls on the Princess's head-dress
with feverish energy and changes it again. The Princess continues to
wear a pensive expression. Valzacchi, followed by Annina, has,
behind the back of everybody else, slunk to the other side of the
stage, and they present themselves to the Baron with exaggerated
obsequiousness.*)

PRINCESS (*over her shoulder to the Major-Domo*):
They are all dismissed.

(Die Lakaien, eine Kette bildend schieben die aufwartenden Personen zur Tür hinaus, die sie dann verschliessen. Nur der Gelehrte, vom Haushofmeister ihr zugeführt bleibt noch im Gespräch m': der Marschallin, bis zum Schluss des Intermezzos zwischen Valzacchi, Annina und dem Baron. Valzacchi, hinter ihm Annina, haben sich im Rücken aller rings um die Bühne zum Baron hinübergeschlichen und präsentieren sich ihm mit übertriebener Devotion).

VALZACCHI *(zum Baron)*:

    Ihre Gnade sukt etwas. Ik seh,
    Ihr Gnade at eine Bedürfnis.
    Ik kann dienen. Ik kann besorgen.

BARON *(tritt zurück)*:

    Wer ist Er, was weiss Er

VALZACCHI   Ihr Gnade Gesikt sprikt ohne Sunge.
    Wie ein Hantike: come statua do Giove.

BARON: Das ist ein besserer Mensch.

VALZACCHI: Erlaukte Gnade, attachieren uns an Sein Gefolge.
            (Fällt auf die Knie, desgleichen Annina.)

BARON: Euch?

VALZACCHI: Onkel und Nikte.
    Su sweien maken alles besser.
    Per esempio: Ihre Gnade at eine junge Frau—

BARON: Woher weiss Er denn das, Er Teufel Er?

VALZACCHI *(eifrig)*:

    Ihre Gnade ist in Eifersukt: dico per dire
    Eut oder morgen könnte sein. Affare nostro!
    Jede Sritt die Dame sie tut,
    jede Wagen die Dame steigt,
    jede Brief die Dame bekommt —
    wir sind da!
    An die Ecke, in die Kamin, 'inter die Bette—
    in eine Schranke, unter die Dache,
    wir sind da!

ANNINA: Ihre Gnaden wird nicht bedauern
    (Halten ihm die Hände hin, Geld heischend, er tut, als bemerke er es nicht.)

BARON *(halblaut)*:

    Hm: Was es alles gibt in diesem Wien?
    Zur Probe nur: kennt Sie die Jungfer Mariandel?

ANNINA *(ebenso)*:

    Mariandel?

BARON *(ebenso)*:

    Das Zofel hier im Haus bei Ihrer Gnaden?

VALZACCHI *(leise zu Annina)*:

    Sai tu, cosa vuole?

(The Footmen, taking hands, push them all out by the door, which they then close. Only the Scholar, whom the Major-Domo presents to the Princess, remains in conversation with her till the close of the episode between the Baron, Valzacchi and Annina.)

VALZACCHI (*to the Baron*):

Is your Lords'ip lacking aught? I see zat your Lords'ip
Is looking for somezing. I can help you, I can be useful.

BARON (*drawing back*):

And who may you be, pray?

VALZACCHI: Zough your Lords'ip say nozzing
Ve understand from your Lords'ip's expression.

ANNINA: Vat your Lords'ip wishes . . .

VALZACCHI: Come statua di Giove.

BARON: He might be useful, I think.

VALZACCHI and ANNINA (*kneeling*):

May't please your Lords'ip we declare ourselves your 'umble
servants.

BARON: You?

VALZACCHI and ANNINA: Uncle and niece
In couples our vork is easier.
Per esempio? 'As your Lords'ip married a youzful
bride . . .

BARON: How come you to know so much, you dog?

VALZACCHI and ANNINA (*eagerly*):

'As your Lords'ip cause for jealousy? Dico per dire.
Now or to-morrow? Who can tell? Affare nostro!
Every step ze lady may take,
Every coach zat ze lady 'ires,
Every billet doux zat she 'as—
Ve are zere
At ze corner, or by ze fire
Or in a cupboard, or in ze attic,
Or by ze bedside, under ze table,
Ve are zere!

ANNINA: Sure your Lords'ip vill not regret it.

(They hold out their hands as if for money. The Baron pretends not to notice them.)

BARON (*aside*):

Hm! What things we see and hear in this great town!
To try your skill, do you perchance know Mariandel?

VALZACCHI: Mariandel?

BARON: Her Highness's waiting maid that's always with her!

VALZACCHI (*aside to Annina*):

Sai tu? Cosa vuole?

39

ANNINA (*ebenso*):
Niente!

VALZACCHI (*zum Baron*):
Sicker! Sicker! Mein nickte wird besorgen.
Seien sicker, Ihre Gnade? Wir sind da!

(*Hält abermals die Hand hin, Baron tut, als sähe er es nicht. Marschallin ist aufgestanden. Friseur nach tiefer Verbeugung eilt ab. Gehilfe hinter ihm.*)

BARON (*die beiden Italiener stehen lassend, auf die Marschallin zu*):
Darf ich das Gegenstück.

(*diskret.*)

zu Dero sauberm Kammerzofel präsentieren?

(*Selbstgefällig.*)

Die Ahnlichgeit soll, hör' ich, unverkennbar sein.

MARSCHALLIN (*nickt*):

BARON:
Leupold, das Futteral.
(*Der junge Kammerlakai präsentiert linkisch das Futteral.*)

MARSCHALLIN (*ein bischen lachend*):
Ich gratulier' Euer Liebden sehr.

BARON (*nimmt dem Burschen das Futteral aus der Hand und winkt ihm zurückzutreten*).
Und da ist nun die silberne Rosen!

(*Will's aufmachen.*)

MARSCHALLIN: Lassen nur drinnen.
Haben die Gnad' und stellen's dort hin.

BARON:
Vielleicht das Zofel soll's übernehmen?
Ruft man ihr?

MARSCHALLIN: Nein, lassen nur. Die hat jetzt keine Zeit.
Doch sei Er sicher: den Grafen Octavian bitt' ich ihm auf,
er wird's mir zulieb schon tun
und als Euer Liebden Kavalier
vorfahren mit der Rosen bei der Jungfer Braut.

(*Leichthin.*)

Stellen indes nur hin.
Und jetzt, Herr Vetter, sag' ich Ihm Adieu.
Man retiriert sich jetzt von hier:
Ich werd' jetzt in die Kirchen gehn.

(*Lakaien öffnen die Flügeltür.*)

BARON:
Euer Gnaden haben heut
durch unversiegte Huld mich tiefst beschämt.

(*Macht die Reverenz; entfernt sich unter Zeremoniell. Der Notar hinter ihm, auf seinen Wink. Seine drei Leute hinter diesem, in mangelhafter Haltung. Die beiden Italiener lautlos und geschmeidig, schlissen sich unbemerkt an. Lakaien schliessen die Tür. Haushofmeister tritt ab. Marschallin allein.*)

ANNINA: Niente.

VALZACCHI (*to the Baron*):

Trust us, trust us: ve vill soon 'ave information—
Put your trust in us, your Lords'ip—
Ve are zere!

BARON (*leaving the two Italians, to the Princess*):

May I now introduce, in all discretion,
The counterpart of your young servant to your Highness?
The likeness is wonderful, my friends all tell me.

(*Princess nods.*)

Leopold, the jewel-case!

PRINCESS (*smiling*):

He does great honour to his ancestry.

(*The young body servant awkwardly hands over the jewel-case.*)

BARON (*taking his seat and signing to the young man to withdraw*):

The Silver Rose is here, in this casket.

(*Opening it.*)

PRINCESS: Do not disturb it.
Pray, place it yonder, I'll be obliged.

BARON: Or shall I call your waiting-maid
And give it to her—

PRINCESS: Not to her. She is now occupied.
But this I promise—I will at once make known your wishes
to the Count,

For me he will consent, I know—
And all proper usage observing,
Duly to your bride the Rose of Silver bear,
Meanwhile I'll keep it here.
And now, your Lordship, I bid you adieu—
It is high time that I should go
Else I shall be too late for church—

(*The Footmen open the folding doors.*)

BARON: The most gracious courtesy your Highness renders me
O'erwhelms me quite—

(*He makes an obeisance and ceremoniously withdraws. At a sign
from him, the Attorney follows; and after him the Baron's three
servants shuffle out awkwardly. The two Italians silently and
obsequiously join the train without his observing them. The
Major-Domo withdraws. The Footmen close the door. The
Princess is left alone.*)

MARSCHALLIN (*allein*):
Da geht er hin, der aufgeblasene schlechte Kerl,
und kriegt das hübsche junge Ding und einen Pinkel Geld
dazu.
(*Seufzend.*)
Als musst's so sein.
Und bildet sich noch ein, dass er es ist, der sich was
vergibt.
Was erzürn' ich mich denn? Ist doch der Lauf der Welt.
Kann mich auch an ein Mädel erinnern,
die frisch aus dem Kloster ist in den heiligen Ehestand
kommandiert word'n.
(*Nimmt den Handspiegel.*)
Wo ist die jetzt? Ja,
(*seufzend.*)
such' dir den Schnee vom vergangenen Jahr:
Das sag' ich so:
(*Ruhig.*)
Aber wie kann das wirklich sein,
dass ich die kleine Resi war
und dass ich auch einmal die alte Frau sein werd'.
Die alte Frau, die alte Marschallin!
„Siegst es, da geht's die alte Fürstin Resi!"
Wie kann denn das geschehen?
Wie macht denn das der liebe Gott?
Wo ich doch immer die gleiche bin.
Und wenn er's schon so machen muss,
warum lasst er mich denn zuschaun dabei
mit gar so klarem Sinn! Warum versteckt er's nicht vor
mir?
Das alles ist geheim, so viel geheim.
Und man ist dazu da, (*seufzend*) dass man's ertragt.
Und in dem "Wie"
(*sehr ruhig.*)
da liegt der ganze Unterschied—

OCTAVIAN (*tritt von rechts ein, in einem Morgenanzug mit Reitstiefeln*).

MARSCHALLIN (*ruhig, mit halbem Lächeln*):
Ach, du bist wieder da!

OCTAVIAN (*zärtlich*):
Und du bist traurig!

MARSCHALLIN: Es is ja schon vorbei. Du weisst ja, wie ich bin.
Ein halb Mal lustig, ein halb Mal traurig.
Ich kann halt meinen Gedanken nicht kommandier'n.

OCTAVIAN: Ich weiss, warum du traurig bist, du Schatz.
Weil du erschrocken bist und Angst gehabt hast.
Hab' ich nicht recht? Gesteh' mir nur:
du hast Angst gehabt,
du Süsse, du Liebe,
um mich, um mich!

PRINCESS: Now go your ways.—Go, vain pretentious profligate!
             And what is your reward? An ample dowry and a pretty
                                                                bride—
             He takes it all, thinking 'tis but his due—
             And boasts that he has greatly honoured her.

                                                        (*Sighs.*)

             But why trouble myself? The world will have its way.
             Did I not know a girl, just like to this one,
             Who straight from out her convent was marched off
             Into the Holy Estate of Wedlock?
             Where is she now!

                                                        (*Sighs.*)

             Go seek the snows of yesteryear!
             But can it be—can it be—though I say it so,
             That I was that young Tess of long ago
             And that I shall be called, ere long, "the old **Princess**,"
             "The Old Field Marshal's lady."—"Look you
             "There goes the old Princess Theresia"—
             How can it come to pass?
             How can the Pow'rs decree it so?
             For I am I, and never change.

                                                        (*Gaily.*)

             And if indeed it must be so,
             Why then must I sit here, a looker on,
             And see it all and grieve? Were it not better we were
                                                                blind?
             These things are still a mystery—a mystery—
             And we are here below to bear it all.

                                                        (*Sighs.*)

             But how? but how?

                                                    (*Very quietly.*)
             In that lies all the difference.

(*Enter Octavian, from the right, in riding dress with riding boots.*)

PRINCESS (*quietly, smiling*):

             Ah! You are back again—

OCTAVIAN: And you are pensive!

PRINCESS: The mood has flown again. You know me, how I am—
             A brief while merry—a brief while mournful—
             My thoughts fly here and there, I know not how.

OCTAVIAN: I know why you have been so sad, belov'd,
             You were beside yourself with fear for us both.
             Is it not so? Confess to me.
             You were sore afraid,
             My angel, my dearest,
             For me—for me!

43

MARSCHALLIN: Ein bissel vielleicht,
aber ich hab' mich erfangen und hab' mir vorgesagt: Es
wird schon nicht dafür stehn.
Und wär's dafür gestanden?

OCTAVIAN (*heiter*):
Und es war kein Feldmarschall,
nur ein spassiger Herr Vetter, und du gehörst mir,
du gehörst mir:

MARSCHALLIN (*erhebt sich, ihn abwehrend*):
Taverl, umarm' Er nicht zu viel.
Wer allzuviel umarmt, der hält nichts fest.

OCTAVIAN (*leidenschaftlich*):
Sag' dass du mir gehörst! Mir!

MARSCHALLIN: Oh, sei Er jetzt sanft, sei Er gescheit und sanft und gut.

OCTAVIAN (*will lebhaft erwidern*).

MARSCHALLIN: Nein, bitt' schön, sei Er nicht, wie alle Männer sind!

OCTAVIAN (*misstrauisch auffahrend*):
Wie alle Männer?

MARSCHALLIN (*schnell gefasst*):
Wie der Feldmarschall und der Vetter Ochs.

OCTAVIAN (*nicht dabei beruhigt*):
Bichette!

MARSCHALLIN (*mit Nachdruck*):
Sei Er nur nicht, wie alle Männer sind.

OCTAVIAN (*zornig*):
Ich weiss nicht, wie alle Männer sind.
(*Plötzlich sanft.*)
Weiss nur, dassich dich lieb hab',
Bichette, sie haben mir dich ausgetauscht.
Bichette, wo ist Sie denn!

MARSCHALLIN (*ruhig*):
Sie ist wohl da, Herr Schatz.

OCTAVIAN: Ja, ist Sie da? Dann will ich Sie halten,
dass Sie mir nicht wieder entkommt!
(*Leidenschaftlich.*)
Packen will ich Sie, packen, dass
Sie es spürt, zu wem Sie gehört —
zu mir: Denn ich bin Ihr und Sie ist mein!

MARSCHALLIN (*sich ihm entwindend*):
Oh, sei Er gut, Quinquin. Mir ist zumut,
dass ich die Schwäche von allem Zeitlichen recht spüren
muss,
bis in mein Herz hinein,
wie man nichts halten soll,
wie man nichts packen kann,
wie alles zerlauft zwischen den Fingern,
alles sich auflöst, wonach wir greifen,
alles zergeht wie Dunst und Traum.

PRINCESS: A little at first,
But soon my courage had come back, and to myself I said—
"It cannot be—'Tis not yet." And if it had been fated?

OCTAVIAN (*gaily*):
And it was not the Prince at all, 'twas only your comical
                                                kinsman.
And you are mine own! You are mine own!

PRINCESS (*pushing him aside*):
Dearest, embrace me not so much!
Who tries to grasp too much, holds nothing fast.

OCTAVIAN (*passionately*):
Tell me that you are mine—mine!

PRINCESS: Oh, be not so wild! Be gentle and tender and kind
No, prithee now—
                    (*Octavian is about to answer excited*
Do you not be like all the other men.

OCTAVIAN (*suspiciously*):
Like all the others?

PRINCESS (*quickly recovering herself*):
As the Marshal is, and as my kinsman Ochs.

OCTAVIAN (*still dissatisfied*):
Bichette!

PRINCESS (*emphatically*):
No—do not be like all the other men.

OCTAVIAN (*angrily*):
The others? How can I know what they are—
                    (*With sudden tenderness.*)
Only I know I love you.
Bichette, there surely is some changeling here.
Bichette, it is not you.

PRINCESS: No, it is I, my dear.

OCTAVIAN: Yes, it is you? Closer will I clasp you,
That you'll never, never escape me,
I will cling to you tightly,
That in truth you will know whose you are.

PRINCESS (*freeing herself from him*):

Command yourself, Mignon. I feel I know
That all things earthly are but vanity, but empty dreams
Deep in my heart I know
How we should grasp at naught,
How we can cling to naught,
How the world's joys cheat and elude us—
How empty all things are that we deem precious,
All things must pass, like mists—like dreams.

Octavian   Mein Gott, wie Sie das sagt.
             Sie will mir doch nur zeigen, dass Sie nicht an mir hängt.
                                    (*Die Tränen kommen ihm.*)

MARSCHALLIN: Sei Er doch gut, Quinquin!

OCTAVIAN (*weint stärker*):

MARSCHALLIN: Jetzt muss ich noch den Buben dafür trösten,
             Dass er mich über kurz oder lang wird sitzen lassen.
                                          (*Sie streichelt ihn.*)
OCTAVIAN: Ueber kurz oder lang?
                                                    (*Heftig.*)
             Wer legt Ihr heut die Wörter in den Mund, Bichette?

MARSCHALLIN: Das Ihn das Wort so kränkt!

OCTAVIAN (*hält sich die Ohren zu*).

MARSCHALLIN: Die Zeit im Grund, Quinquin,
             Die Zeit, die ändert doch nichts an den Sachen.
             Die Zeit, die ist ein sonderbar Ding.
             Wenn man so hinlebt, ist sie rein gar nichts.
             Aber dann auf einmal, da spürt man nichts als sie.
             Sie ist um uns herum, sie ist auch in uns drinnen.
             In den Gesichtern rieselt sie,
             im Spiegel da rieselt sie,
             in meinen Schläfen fliesst sie.
             Und zwischen mir und dir
             da fliesst sie wieder, lautlos, wie eine Sanduhr.
                                                    (*Warm.*)
             Oh, Quinquin!   Manchmal hör' ich sie fliessen —
             unaufhaltsam.
                                                    (*Leise.*)
             Manchmal steh' ich auf mitten in der Nacht
             und lass die Uhren alle, alle stehn.
             Allein man muss sich auch vor ihr nicht fürchten.
             Auch sie ist ein Geschöpf des Vaters, der uns alle erschaffen
                                                          hat.
OCTAVIAN (*mit ruhiger Zärtlichkeit*):
             Mein schöner Schatz, will Sie sich traurig machen mit
                                                          Gewalt?
             Wo Sie mich da hat.
             wo ich meine Finger in Ihre Finger schlinge,
             wo ich mit meinen Augen Ihre Augen suche,
             Wo sie mich hat —
             gerade da ist Ihr so zumut?

MARSCHALLIN (*sehr ernst*):
             Quinquin, heut oder morgen geht Er hin
             und gibt mich auf um einer andern willen,
                                          (*etwas zögernd.*)
             die schöner oder jünger ist als ich.

46

OCTAVIAN: Oh Heav'n! Why so distraught,
              You do but want to tell me that your love is dead.
                                                    (*Weeps.*)

PRINCESS: Be not so sad, Mignon.
                         (*Octavian weeps more passionately.*)
                                                    (*Quietly.*)
              And now must I for him find consolation—
              And for what? Because—sooner or later—one day he'll
                                                    leave me.
                                              (*Strokes his hair.*)

OCTAVIAN: I will leave you one day?
                                                    (*Angrily.*)
              Who is it prompted you to talk of this?

PRINCESS: Do my words hurt you so?

OCTAVIAN: Bichette!

PRINCESS: What fate decrees must come, Mignon.
                               (*Octavian stops his ears.*)
              And time—how strangely does it go its ways—
              First we are heedless—Lo! 'tis as nothing!
              Then a sudden waking, and we feel naught else but it,
              All the world tells of it, all our souls are filled with it,
              No face but shows the mark of it,
              No mirror but shows it us—
              All my veins feel its throbbing,
              And there—'twixt you and me—
              It flows in silence,
              Trickling—like sands in the hour-glass—
                                                    (*Earnestly.*)
              Oh! Mignon!
              But sometimes I hear it flowing
              Ceaselessly.
                                                    (*Softly.*)
              Sometimes I arise at the dead of night
              And take the clocks and stop them ev'ry one—
              And yet—to be afraid of it—what boots it?
              For, mindful of its creatures all. Heav'n in its own wisdom
                                              has ordained it so.

OCTAVIAN (*quietly and tenderly*):
              And why let such dark forebodings cloud your soul, belov'd?
              Now that I am here,
              With my fingers like tendrils round your fingers twining,
              Now that mine eyes are plunged in yours and blaze with
                                                    rapture,
              Now that I am here,
              At such time can you think of grief?

PRINCESS (*very serious*):
              Mignon, now or to-morrow, surely.
              You will go from me, leave me and choose another.
                                                    (*Hesitates.*)
              A younger or a prettier than I.

OCTAVIAN: Willst du mit Worten mich von dir stossen,
weil dir die Hände den Dienst nicht tun?

MARSCHALLIN (*ruhig*):
Der Tag kommt ganz von selber.
Heut oder morgen kommt der Tag, Octavian.

OCTAVIAN: Nicht heut, nicht morgen! ich hab dich lieb.
Nicht heut, nicht morgen!
Wenn's so einen Tag geben muss, i denk' ihn nicht!
So einen hässlichen Tag!
Ich will den Tag nicht sehn
Ich will den Tag nicht denken.
Was quälst du dich und mich, Theres'?

MARSCHALLIN: Heut oder morgen oder den übernächsten Tag.
Nicht quälen will ich dich, mein Schatz.
Ich sag' was wahr ist, sag's zu mir so gut als zu dir.
Leicht will ich's machen dir und mir.
Leicht muss man sein,
mit leichtem Herz und leichten Händen
halten und nehmen, halten und lassen . . .
Die nicht so sind, die straft das Leben, und Gott erbarn
sich ihrer nicht.

OCTAVIAN: Sie spricht ja heute wie ein Pater.
Soll dass heissen, dass ich Sie nie mehr
werd' küssen dürfen, bis Ihr der Atem ausgeht?

MARSCHALLIN (*sanft*):
Quinquin, Er soll jetzt gehn, Er soll mich lassen.
Ich werd' jetzt in die Kirchen gehn,
und später fahr' ich zum Onkel Greifenklau,
der alt und gelähmt ist,
und ess' mit ihm: das freut den alten Mann.
Und Nachmittag werd' ich Ihm einen Laufer schicken,
Quinquin, und sagen lassen,
ob ich in' Prater fahr'.
Und wenn ich fahr'
und Er hat Lust,
so wird Er auch in' Prater kommen
und neben meinem Wagen reiten.
Jetzt sei Er gut und folg' Er mir.

OCTAVIAN (*leise*):
Wie Sie befiehlt, Bichette.

(*Er geht. Eine Pause*)

MARSCHALLIN (*allein, fährt leidenschaftlich auf*):
Ich hab' Ihn nicht einmal geküsst.

(*Sie klingelt heftig. Lakaien kommen von rech.*)

MARSCHALLIN: Lauft's dem Herrn Grafen nach
und bittet's ihn noch auf ein Wort herauf.

LAKAIEN (*schnell ab*).

MARSCHALLIN: Ich hab' ihn fortgehn lassen und ihn nicht einmal geküsst.
(*Sie sinkt auf den Sessel am Frisiertisch. Die Lakaien kommen
zurück ausser Atem.*)

OCTAVIAN: Is it with words from hence you would drive me,
            Thinking your hands will not serve your turn?

PRINCESS   (*quietly*):
            The day will come unbidden—
            Now or tomorrow it must come, Octavian.

OCTAVIAN: Not now, not to-morrow—'twill never come,
            Though Fate have decreed it must come, I will not think
            Nor see such a day,
            I will not think such a day,

                              (*With growing passion.*)
            I will not see nor think it!
            Why torture me and yourself, Thérèse?

PRINCESS: Now or to-morrow—if not to-morrow, very soon—
            'Tis not to torture you, my dearest,
            'Tis truth that I'm speaking—to myself no less than to you.
            Let us then lightly meet our fate.
            Light must we be,
            With spirits light and grasp light-fingered,
            Hold all our pleasures—hold them and leave them.
            If not, much pain and grief await us, and none in earth or
                                            heav'n will pity us.

OCTAVIAN: You speak to-day like a confessor—
            Does it mean that never again—no, never,
            I shall kiss you—kiss you in endless rapture?

PRINCESS: Mignon, now you must go. 'Tis time to leave me.
            I now must go to Church, and then
            It may be, visit my dear uncle Greifenklau,
            Who's old and bedridden,
            And dine with him: 'twill please the old man much.
            Then to your house I'll send a courier,
            Mignon, and he will tell you
            Whether I shall take the air;
            And if I drive,
            And if you please,
            You will meet me in the Prater, riding,
            And stay awhile beside my carriage.
            Do what I ask—and be not rash.

OCTAVIAN   (*softly*):
            As you command, Bichette.

                              (*He goes. A pause.*)
                              (*The Princess starts up violently.*)

PRINCESS: And he has gone, and not one kiss!
         (*She rings violently. Footmen enter hurriedly from the right.*)
            Run and o'ertake the Count
            And say I beg a word with him.
                              (*Exeunt Footmen quickly.*)
            I have let him go from me. No farewell—not one kiss!
                              (*The four Footmen enter breathless.*)

ERSTER LAKAI: Der Herr Graf sind auf und davon.

ZWEITER LAKAI: Gleich beim Tor sind aufgesess.

DRITTER LAKAI: Reitknecht hat gewartet.

VIERTER LAKAI: Gleich beim Tor sind aufgesessen wie der Wind.

ERSTER LAKAI: Waren um die Ecken wie der Wind.

ZWEITER LAKAI: Sind nachgelaufen.

DRITTER LAKAI: Wie haben wir geschrien.

VIERTER LAKAI: War umsonst.

ERSTER LAKAI: Waren um die Ecken wie der Wind.

MARSCHALLIN: Es ist gut, geht's nur wieder.
(Die Lakaien ziehen sich zurück.)

MARSCHALLIN *(ruft nach)*:
Den Mohammed!
(Der kleine Neger herein, klingelnd, verneigt sich.)

MARSCHALLIN: Das da trag'.

NEGER *(nimmt eifrig das Saffianfutteral)*.

MARSCHALLIN: Weisst ja nicht wohin. Zum Grafen Octavian.
Gib's ab und sag':
Da drin ist die silberne Ros'n.
Der Herr Graf weiss ohnehin.
(Der Neger läuft ab.)

MARSCHALLIN *(stützt den Kopf auf die Hand und bleibt so während des ganzen Nachspiels)*.

FIRST FOOTMAN: The young Count is off and away.

SECOND FOOTMAN: At the door he mounted quickly.

THIRD FOOTMAN: Servants had been in waiting—

FOURTH FOOTMAN: At the gate he mounted like the wind—

FIRST FOOTMAN: Galloped round the corner like the wind—

SECOND FOOTMAN: We all ran after—

THIRD FOOTMAN: We cried ourselves hoarse—

FOURTH FOOTMAN: 'Twas too late.

FIRST FOOTMAN: Galloped round the corner like the wind—

PRINCESS: Very well. You may leave me.

> *(The Footmen withdraw.)*

PRINCESS *(calling after them)*:
>   Send Mahomet.
>
>   *(Enter the Black Boy, with tinkling bells. Bows.)*

PRINCESS: Carry that—

>   *(The Boy quickly takes the jewel case.)*

>   Stop till I say where—To Count Octavian
>   And say he'll find
>   Within it the Silver Rose
>   'Tis enough—the Count will know.

(The Black Boy runs off. The Princess bows her head on her hand and remains so—deep in thought—till the curtain falls.)

END OF ACT I.

ZWEITER AUFZUG

Saal bei Herrn von Faninal. Mitteltüre nach dem Vorsaal. Tür links. Rechts ein grosses Fenster. Stühle an der Wand. In den Ecken jederseits grosse Kamine. Zu beiden Seiten der Mitteltüre je ein Lakai.

FANINAL (*im Begriffe, von Sophie Abschied zu nehmen*):
Ein ernster Tag, ein grosser Tag!
Ein Ehrentag, ein heiliger Tag!

SOPHIE (*küsst ihm die Hand*).

MARIANNE: Der Josef fahrt vor mit der neuen Kaross',
hat himmelblaue Vorhäng',
vier Apfelschimmel sind dran.

HAUSHOFMEISTER (*nicht ohne Vertraulichkeit zu Faninal*):
Ist höchste Zeit, dass Euer Gnaden fahren.
Der hochadelige Bräutigamsvater,
sagt die Schicklichkeit,
muss ausgefahren sein
bevor der silberne Rosenkavalier vorfahrt.
Wär nicht geziemend,
dass sie sich vor der Tür begegneten.

                       (*Lakaien öffnen die Tür.*)

FANINAL: In Gottes Namen. Wenn ich wiederkomm',
so führ' ich deinen Herrn Zukünftigen bei der Hand.

MARIANNE: Den edlen und gestrengen Herrn von Lerchenau!

FANINAL (*geht*).

SOPHIE (*vorgehend, allein, indessen Marianne am Fenster*).

MARIANNE: Jetzt steigt er ein. Der Xaver und der Anton springen
                                   hinten auf.
Der Stallpag' reicht dem Josef seine Peitsch'n.
Alle Fenster sind voller Leut'.

SOPHIE (*am Fenster*):
In dieser feierlichen Stunde der Prüfung,
da du mich, o mein Schöpfer, über mein Verdienst erhöhen
und in den heiligen Ehestand führen willst,
       (*sie hat grosse Mühe, gesammelt zu bleiben*)
opfere ich dir in Demut, mein Herz in Demut auf.
Die Demut in mir zu erwecken,
muss ich mich demütigen.

MARIANNE: Die halbe Stadt ist auf die Füss'.
Aus dem Seminari schaun die Hochwürdigen von die
                                   Balkoner
Ein alter Mann sitzt oben auf der Latern'.

ACT TWO

A room in the house of Herr von Faninal. Centre door leading to the antechamber. Doors right and left. To the right a large window. At either side of the centre door chairs against the wall. In the rounded corners at either side large fireplaces.

HERR VON FANINAL (*in the act of saying goodbye to Sophia*):
A solemn day, a day of no
A festal day, a sacred day

                (*Sophia kisses his hand.*)

MARIANNE:
There's Joseph at the door with the new equipage,
With curtains of blue satin.
And four fine greys to draw it.

MAJOR DOMO (*a little confidentially to Faninal*):
Now by your leave, Sir, 'tis high time for starting,
For the most noble father of the bride,—
So etiquette prescribes—
Must not be found within,
When the bridegroom's messenger appears who brings the
                Silver Rose.

FANINAL:
Well then, so be it.

              (*Footmen open the doors.*)

MAJOR-DOMO:
'Twould be unseemly
If at the door you should encounter him.

FANINAL:
When I return again,
I bring your bridegroom with me, holding him by the
              hand.

MARIANNE:
The virtuous and noble Lord of Lerchenau.

              (*Exit Faninal.*)

(*Sophia advances to the front by herself, while Marianne is at the window.*)

MARIANNE:
Now he's got in. Now Antony and Francis have climbed
              up behind,
And Joseph cracks his whip and now they've started,
And all the windows are filled full of folk.

SOPHIA:
In this most sacred hour, my God, O my Creator,
When Thy great blessings lift me high above my worth,
              I thank Thee,
That to the Holy Estate by Thy will I am led.
          (*She controls herself with difficulty.*)
A contrite heart unto Thy Throne—Thy Throne—I bring.
Oh! Grant that the sin of vainglory
May ever be far from my soul.

MARIANNE (*very excited*):
Half the Town is now afoot!
From the Seminary all the reverend men look on dumb-
              founded,
And high up on a lantern there is one old man.

SOPHIE (*sammelt sich mühsam*):
Demütigen und recht bedenken: die Sünde, die
Schuld, die Niedrigkeit, die Verlassenheit, die Anfechtung!
Die Mutter ist tot und ich bin ganz allein.
Für mich selbst steh' ich ein.
Aber die Ehe ist ein heiliger Stand.

MARIANNE (*wie oben*):
Er kommt, er kommt in zwei Karossen.
Die erste ist vierspännig, die ist leer. In der zweiten,
sechsspännigen,
sitzt er selber, der Rosenkavalier.

SOPHIE (*wie oben*):
Ich will mich niemals meines neuen Standes überheben —
(*die Stimmen der Läufer zu dreien vor Octavians Wagen unten auf
der Gasse: Rofrano, Rofrano!*)
— mich überheben.
(*Sie hält es nicht aus.*)
Was rufen denn die?

MARIANNE: Den Namen vom Rosenkavalier und alle Namen
von deiner neuen fürstlich'n und gräflich'n Verwandtschaft
rufen's aus.
Jetzt rangieren sich die Bedienten.
Die Lakaien springen rückwärts ab!
(*Die Stimmen der Läufer zu dreinen näher: Rofrano, Rofrano!*)

SOPHIE: Werden sie mein' Bräutigam sein Namen
auch so ausrufen, wenn er angefahren kommt!?
(*Die Stimmen der Läufer dicht unter dem Fenster: Rofrano, Rofrano!*)

MARIANNE: Sie reissen den Schlag auf! Er steigt aus!
Ganz in Silberstück' ist er angelegt, von Kopf zu Fuss.
Wie ein heil'ger Engel schaut er aus.
(*Sie schliesst eilig das Fenster. Zwei Faninalsche Lakaien haben
schnell die Mitteltür aufgetan.*)

SOPHIE: Herrgott im Himmel!
Ich weiss, der Stolz ist eine schwere Sünd'.
Aber jetzt kann ich mich nicht demütigen.
Jetzt seht's halt nicht!
Denn das ist ja so schön, so schön!

(*Währenddem ist Octavians Dienerschaft in seinen Farben; weiss
mit blassgrün rasch eingetreten. Die Lakaien, die Haiducken
mit krummen ungarischen Säbeln an der Seite, die Läufer in
weissem sämischem Leder mit grünen Straussenfedern. Dicht
hinter diesen ein Neger, der Octavians Hut, und ein anderer Lakai,
der das Saffianfutteral für die silberne Rose in beiden Händen
trägt. Dann Octavian, die Rose in der Rechten. Er geht mit
adeligem Anstand auf Sophie zu, aber sein Knabengesicht ist von
seiner Schüchternheit gespannt und gerötet. Sophie ist vor
Aufregung über seine Erscheinung und die Zeremonie leichen-
blass. Sie stehen einander gegenüber, und machen sich wechsel-
weise durch ihre Verlegenheit und Schönheit noch verwirrter.*)*

54

SOPHIA (*collects her thoughts with difficulty*):

> Be far from my soul . . .
> From all temptations, Lord, preserve me of the pomps and
> > vanities
> Of this world here below, by Thy great mercy—
> My Mother, she is dead and all alone am I,
> For me there's none to plead but I alone,
> But wedlock is in truth a holy estate.

MARIANNE (*at the window*):

> He is here! He's here! I see two coaches.
> The first one has four horses—it is empty. In the second,
> (Six horses it has)
> I see him, the bridegroom's messenger.

SOPHIA (*as above*):

> Let me not be puffed up with pride unduly by the honours,

> (*The servants followed by three couriers, who are running after
> Octavian's carriage, cry in the street below "Rofrano! Rofrano!"*)
> > (*She loses her self-control.*)
> Of my new station.
> What is it they cry?

MARIANNE: They're shouting the name of him that's come and all the
> > titles
> Of this your high-born new relation, and his noble name.
> > (*With excited gestures.*)

> Look! Now our footmen take position,
> And all his servants have alighted now!

(*The voices of the couriers, drawing nearer: "Rofrano! Rofrano!"*)

SOPHIA: And when my future husband comes, pray tell me,
> Will they call out then? Will his name be shouted too?

(*The voices of the couriers immediately under the window: "Rofrano! Rofrano!"*

MARIANNE (*enthusiastically*):

> They open the door now! He alights!
> All in silver he glitters from head to foot,
> A holy angel might he be—

SOPHIA: Ye Saints in Heaven, I know that pride is a most deadly
> > sin;

> But this day all my prayers are vain—I cannot
> Be duly meek—
> For it is all so fair! So fair!

(*The Footmen quickly open the centre door. Enter Octavian bare-
headed, dressed all in white and silver, carrying the Silver Rose
in his hand. Behind him his servants in his colours—white and
pale green, the Footmen, the Heyducks, with their crooked
Hungarian swords at their side; the Couriers in white leather
with green ostrich plumes. Immediately behind Octavian a
black servant carrying his hat, and another Footman carrying
the case of the Silver Rose in both hands. Behind these, Faninal's
servants. Octavian taking the Rose in his right hand, advances
with high-born grace towards Sophia; but his youthful features
bear traces of embarrassment and he blushes. Sophia turns pale
with excitement at his splendid appearance. They stand opposite each other—each disconcerted by the confusion and beauty
of the other.*)

55

OCTAVIAN (*etwas stockend*):

> Mir ist die Ehre widerfahren,
> dass ich der hoch- und wohlgeborenen Jungfer Braut,
> in meines Herrn Vetters Namen,
> dessen zu Lerchenau,
> die Rose seiner Liebe überreichen darf.

SOPHIE (*nimmt die Rose*):

> Ich bin Euer Liebden sehr verbunden.—
> Ich bin Euer Liebden in aller Ewigkeit verbunden.—
>
> (*Einer Pause der Verwirrung.*)

SOPHIE (*indem sie an der Rose riecht*):

> Hat einen starken Geruch. Wie Rosen, wie lebendige.

OCTAVIAN: Ja, ist ein Tropfen persischen Rosenöls darein getan.

SOPHIE: Wie himmelische, nicht irdische, wie Rosen
> vom hochheiligen Paradies. Ist Ihm nicht auch?

OCTAVIAN (*neigt sich über die Rose, die sie ihm hinhält; dann richtet er sich auf und sieht auf ihren Mund*).

SOPHIE: Ist wie ein Gruss vom Himmel. Ist bereits zu stark, als dass
> man's ertragen kann.
> Zieht einen nach, als lägen Stricke um das Herz.
>
> (*Leise.*)
>
> Wo war ich schon einmal
> und war so selig?

OCTAVIAN (*zugleich mit ihr wie unbewusst und noch leiser*).
> Wo war ich schon einmal
> und war so selig?

SOPHIE (*mit Ausdruck*):

> Dahin muss ich zurück! und müsst ich völlig sterben auf
> dem Weg!
> Allein ich sterb' ja nicht.
> Das ist ja weit. Ist Zeit und Ewigkeit
> in einem sel'gen Augenblick,
> den will ich nie vergessen bis an meinen Tod.

OCTAVIAN (*zugleich mit ihr*):

> Ich war ein Bub',
> da hab ich' die noch nicht gekannt.
> Wer bin denn ich?
> Wie komm' denn ich zu ihr?
> Wie kommt denn sie zu mir?
> Wär' ich kein Mann, die Sinne möchten mir vergehn.
> Das ist ein seliger Augenblick,
> den will ich nie vergessen bis an meinen Tod.

(*Indessen stand die Livree Octavians rückwärts regungslos. Ebenso die Faninalschen Bedienten mit dem Haushofmeister. Der Lakai Octavians übergibt jetzt das Futteral an Marianne. Sophie schüttelt ihre Versunkenheit ab und reicht die Rose der Marianne, die sie ins Futteral schliesst. Der Lakai mit dem Hut tritt von rückwärts an Octavian heran und reicht ihm den Hut. Die Livree Octavians tritt ab, während gleichzeitig die Faninalschen Bedienten drei Stühle in die Mitte tragen, zwei für Octavian und*

OCTAVIAN (*with slight hesitation*):

> I am much honoured by my mission
> To say to you, most noble lady, high-born bride,
> That my dear kinsman, whose ambassador I am,
> Baron Lerchenau, begs you
> To take from me, as token of his love, this Rose.

SOPHIA (*taking the Rose*):

> I am to your Honour much indebted—
> I am to your Honour to all eternity indebted—
>
> > (*A short pause of confusion.*)

SOPHIA (*smelling the rose*):

> 'Tis a fragrance entrancing—like roses—yes, like living
> ones. . . .

OCTAVIAN: Yes—some few drops of Persian attar have been poured
thereon.

SOPHIA: A celestial flower, not of earth it seems.
A blossom from the sacred groves of Paradise.
Think you not so?

(*Octavian bends over the Rose, which she holds out to him; then raises his head and gazes at her lips.*)

> 'Tis like a heavenly message.—Oh! how strong the scent
> I scarce can suffer it,
>
> > (*Softly.*)
> Drawing me on—like something tugging at my heart.

OCTAVIAN (*together with her—as in a reverie—still more softly*):

> Where did I taste of old
> Such rapture celestial?

SOPHIA: Though death await me there, to that fair scene I must
betake me once again.
But yet, why think of death?
'Tis far from hence!
In one blest moment dwells all life and all eternity—
Ne'er may its mem'ry fade!

OCTAVIAN: I was a child
Till her fair face I saw this day!
But who am I?
What fate brings her to me?
What fate brings me to her?
Feeling and sense would leave me,
Were I not a man.
Day blest to all eternity—
Ne'er may its blessing fade.

(*During this, Octavian's servants have taken up their position on the left at the back, Faninal's with the Major-Domo to the right. Octavian's footman hands the jewel case to Marianne. Sophia wakes from her reverie and gives the Rose to Marianne. who encloses it in the case. The Footman with the hat approaches Octavian and gives it to him. Octavian's servants then withdraw, and at the same time Faninal's servants carry* **three chairs to the centre, two for Sophia and Octavian, and**)

Sophie, einen rück- und seitwärts für die Duenna. Zugleich trägt
der Faninalsche Haushofmeister das Futteral mit der Rose durch
die Tür links ab. Sofort treten auch die Faninalschen Bedienten
durch die Mitteltür ab. Sophie und Octavian stehen einander
gegenüber, einigermassen zur gemeinen Welt zurückgekehrt, aber
befangen. Auf einer Handbewegung Sophies nehmen sie beide
Platz, desgleichen die Duenna, im gleichen Augenblick, wo der
Haushofmeister unsichtbar die Tür links von aussen zuschliesst.)

SOPHIE: Ich kenn', Ihn schon recht wohl, mon cousin!

OCTAVIAN: Sie kennt mich, ma cousine?

SOPHIE: Ja, aus dem Buch, wo die Stammerbäume drin sind,
Dem Ehrenspiegel Oesterreichs.
Das nehm' ich immer abends mit ins Bett
und such' mir meine künftige Verwandtschaft drin zusammen.

OCTAVIAN: Tut Sie das, ma cousine?

SOPHIE: Ich weiss, wie alt Euer Liebden sind:
Siebzehn Jahr' und zwei Monat'.
Ich weiss all Ihre Taufnamen: Octavian, Maria, Ehrenreich,
Bonaventura, Ferdinand, Hyacinth.

OCTAVIAN: So gut weiss ich sie selber nicht einmal.

SOPHIE: Ich weiss noch was.

(Errötet.)

OCTAVIAN: Was weiss Sie noch, sag' Sie mir's, ma cousine.

SOPHIE (*ohne ihn anzusehen*):
Quinquin.

OCTAVIAN (*lacht*)
Weiss Sie den Namen auch?

SOPHIE: So nennen Ihn halt seine guten Freund'
und schöne Damen, denk' ich mir,
mit denen er recht gut ist.

(Kleine Pause.)

SOPHIE (*mit Naivität*):
Ich freu' mich aufs heiraten! Freut er sich auch darauf?
Oder hat Er leicht noch gar nicht dran gedacht, mon
cousin?
Denk' Er: Ist doch was andres als der ledige Stand.

OCTAVIAN (*leise, während sie spricht*):
Wie schön sie ist!

SOPHIE: Freilich, Er ist ein Mann, da ist Er, was Er bleibt.
Ich aber brauch' erst einen Mann, dass ich was bin.
Dafür bin ich dem Mann dann auch gar sehr verschuldet.

OCTAVIAN (*wie oben*):
Mein Gott, wie schön und gut sie ist.
Sie macht mich ganz verwirrt.

one for *Marianne further back, at the side. Faninal's Major-*
Domo carries the jewel-case with the Rose through the door
to the right. The other servants immediately withdraw through
the centre door.)

(Sophia and Octavian stand opposite each other almost restored
to the every day world—but still a little embarrassed. At a sign
from Sophia, both seat themselves, and the Duenna does like-
wise at the same moment as the door on the right is locked
from without.)

SOPHIA: You're quite well known to me, mon cher Cousin.

OCTAVIAN: You know me, ma Cousine?

SOPHIA: Yes, your great House I have read of in a book,
"The Mirror of Nobility."
I take it of an evening to my room,
And seek for all the Princes, Dukes and Counts
Who are to be my kinsfolk.

OCTAVIAN: Is it so, ma Cousine?

SOPHIA: I know how old, to a week, you are—
Seventeen years and a quarter—
I know all your baptismal names—
Octavian—Maria—Ehrenreich—Bonaventura — Fernand—
Hyacinth.

OCTAVIAN: Faith, I have never known them half as well.

SOPHIA: I know also—

OCTAVIAN: And what is it you know besides, ma Cousine?

SOPHIA (*without looking at him*):
Mignon—

OCTAVIAN (*laughing*):
Do you know that name too?

SOPHIA: So all your best friends are allowed to call you,
Court beauties also, more than one,
Who are with you most friendly.
(*A short pause.*)
(*Naively.*)

It pleases me that I shall marry soon.
Will you not like it too
When you shall find a bride? Have you not thought of
it, mon Cousin?
But think, how lonely all you bachelors are!

OCTAVIAN (*softly*):
Oh heaven! How fair and good she is!

SOPHIA: Truly, you are a man, and men are what they are.
But, till a husband is her guide, a woman's naught.
For these things to my husband I'll be much indebted.

OCTAVIAN (*deeply moved—softly*):
How good and fair she is.
She confuses me quite.

59

SOPHIE: Und werd' ihm keine Schand nicht machen
und meinen Rang und Vortritt.
Tät' eine, die sich besser dünkt als ich,
ihn mir bestreiten
bei einer Kindstauf' oder Leich',
so will ich, wenn es sein muss,
meiner Seel' ihr beweisen,
dass ich die Vornehmere bin
und lieber alles hinnehme
wie Kränkung oder Ungebühr.

OCTAVIAN (*lebhaft*).

Wie kann Sie denn nur denken,
dass man Ihr mit Ungebühr begegnen wird,
da Sie doch immer die Schönste, die Allerschönste sein
wird.

SOPHIE: Lacht er mich aus, mon cousin?

OCTAVIAN: Wie, glaubt Sie das von mir?

SOPHIE: Er darf mich auslachen, wenn er will.
Von Ihm lass ich alles mir gerne geschehen,
weil mir nie noch ein junger Kavalier ....
von Nähen oder Weitem also wohlgefallen hat wie Er.
Jetzt aber kommt mein Herr Zukünftiger.

(*Die Tür rückwärts geht auf. Alle drei erheben sich. Sophie und
Marianne treten nach rechts. Octavian nach links vorne. Faninal führt den Baron zeremoniös über die Schwelle und auf Sophie
zu indem er ihm den Vortritt lässt. Die Lerchenausche Livree
folgt auf Schritt und Tritt: zuerst der Almosenier mit dem
Sohn und Leibkammerdie er. Dann folgt der Leibjäger mit
einem ähnlichen Lümmel, der ein Pflaster über der eingeschlagenen
Nase trägt, und noch zwei von der gleichen Sorte vom Rübenacker
her in die Livree gesteckt. Alle tragen wie ihr Herr Myrthen-
sträusschen. Die zwei Faninalischen Boten bleiben im Hintergrunde.*)

FANINAL: Ich präsentiere Euer Gnaden Dero Zukünftige.

BARON (*macht die Reverenz, dann zu Faninal*):
Deliziös! Mach' Ihm mein Kompliment.
        (*Er küsst Sophie die Hand, gleichsam prüfend.*)
Ein feines Handgelenk. Darauf halt' ich gar viel.
Ist unter Bürgerlichen eine seltne Distinktion.

OCTAVIAN (*halblaut*):
Es wird mir heiss und kalt.

FANINAL: Gestatten dass ich die getreue Jungfer
Marianne Leitmetzerin —
        (*Mariannen präsentierend, die dreimal tief knickst.*)
BARON (*indem er unwillig abwinkt*):
Lass Er das weg.
Begrüss Er jetzt mit mir meinen Herrn Rosenkavalier.

(*Er tritt mit Faninal auf Octavian zu, unter Reverenz, die Octavian
erwiedert. Das Lerchenausche Gefolge kommt endlich zum Still-
stand, nachdem es Sophie fast umgestossen, und retiriert sich um
ein paar Schritte nach rechts rückwärts.*)

SOPHIA : I never will, for sure, disgrace him—
And as for due precedence

(very eagerly)

If haply another woman ever should
Dare to dispute it—
At christenings or funerals—
I'll show her very quickly,
If needs must, with a slapping,
That I am better bred than she,
And rather will bear anything
Than such o'erweening impudence.

OCTAVIAN *(eagerly)* :
Nay, do not think there's anyone
So graceless who would put a slight on you.
For you will still be the fairest, always the crown you
will bear.

SOPHIA : Mock me not so, mon Cousin—

OCTAVIAN : What, think you thus of me?

SOPHIA : You are allowed such freedom, if you will,
From you I gladly take all that you choose.
For, truthfully, no gentleman I've seen
Or met with, has been able yet to please me half as well
as you.
Now I must cease, for look, the Baron's here.

(The door at the back is thrown open. All three rise and step to the right. Faninal ceremoniously conducts the Baron over the threshold towards Sophia, giving him the precedence. The servants of Lerchenau follow in his footsteps, first the Almoner, then the Body Servant. Next follows the Chasseur, with a clown of the same kidney, who has a plaster over his battered nose, and two others no less uncouth, looking as if they had stepped straight from the fields into their liveries. All, like their master, carry sprigs of myrtle. The servants of Faninal remain in the background.)

FANINAL : I have the honour to your Lordship to present your bride.

BARON *(bows—then to Faninal)* :
Délicieuse ! I compliment you, Sir.
(He kisses Sophia's hand as though examining it.)
A hand so delicate is a thing I much admire.
'Tis an attraction rarely found among the *bourgeoisie*.

OCTAVIAN *(to himself)* :
Can I command myself?

FANINAL : Permit me my most faithful friend and servant—
(Presenting Marianne, who makes three deep curtseys.)

BARON *(with a gesture of vexation)* :
Pray, spare me that.

(After having almost knocked Sophia over, Lerchenau's servants come to a standstill, and then withdraw a few paces.)
Now greet the Count, and thank him for being my
ambassador.
(They go towards Octavian, bowing. He returns the compliment.)

61

SOPHIE (*mit Marianne rechtsstehend, halblaut*):

> Was sind das für Manieren? Ist er leicht ein Rosstauscher
> und kommt ihm vor, er hätt' mich eingekauft?

MARIANNE (*ebenso*):

> Ein Kavalier hat halt ein ungezwungenes,
> leutseliges Betragen.
> Sag' dir vor, wer er ist
> und zu was er dich macht,
> so werden dir die Faxen gleich vergehn.

BARON (*während des Aufführens zu Faninal*):

> Ist gar zum Staunen, wie der junge Herr jemand Gewissem
>   ähnlich sieht.
> Hat ein Bastardl, recht ein saubres, zur Schwester.
> Ist kein Geheimnis unter Personen von Stand.
> Hab's aus der Fürstin eignem Mund,
> und weil der Faninal sozusagen jetzo
> zu der Verwandtschaft gehört!
> Mach' dir kein Depit, darum Rofrano,
> dass dein Vater ein Streichmacher war,
> befindet sich dabei in guter Kompagnie, der selige Marchese.
> Ich selber exkludier' mich nicht.
>   (*Zu Octavian.*)
> Seh', Liebden, schau' dir dort den Langen an,
> den Blonden, hinten dort.
> Ich will ihn nicht mit Fingern weisen,
> aber er sticht wohl hervor
> durch eine adelige Kontenance.
> Ist auch er ein ganz besondrer Kerl.
> Sag's nicht, weil ich der Vater bin,
> hat's aber faustdick hinter den Ohren.

SOPHIE (*während dessen*):

> Jetzt lässt er mich so stehn, der grobe Ding!
> Und das **ist** mein Zukünftiger.
> Und blattersteppig ist er auch, o mein Gott!

(*Der Haushofmeister tritt verbindlich auf die Lerchenauschen Leute
zu und führt sie ab. Desgleichen tritt die Faninalsche Livree ab
bis auf zwei, welche Wein und Süssigkeiten servieren.*)

FANINAL (*zum Baron*):

> Belieben jetzt vielleicht? — ist ein alter Tokaier.
>   (*Octavian und Baron bedienen sich.*)

BARON:

> Brav, Faninal, er weiss, was sich gehört.
> Serviert einen alten Tokaier zu einem jungen Mädel.
> Ich bin mit Ihm zufrieden.
>   (*Zu Octavian.*)
> Musst denen Bagatelladeligen immer zeigen,
> dass nicht für unsersgleichen sich ansehen dürfen,
> muss immer was von Herablassung dabei sein.

SOPHIA (*standing at the back with Marianne*):
How vulgar his behaviour. Like some low horse-dealer
Who thinks he's bought me like a yearling colt.

MARIANNE: Oh what an air! How free from affectation,
How full of grace is his behaviour!
Tell yourself who he is,
What he helps you to be
And soon your silly whimsies will be gone.

BARON (*to Faninal*):
I can but wonder, when I see his face,
How like he is to someone else.
Has a sister—most bewitching young baggage.
(*Coarsely confidential.*)
These are no secrets among persons of our rank,
It was her Highness who did tell me so,
(*Genially.*)
And now you, Faninal, may be accounted almost as being
one of us.
There is no need to be ashamed, Rofrano,
That once your father chose to sow wild oats—
I warrant you he was in noble company,
(*Laughing.*)
The late lamented Marquis—I count my self among it, too.
(*To Faninal.*)
Look well now at that long-legged rascal there,
The fair one at the back.
I cannot point my finger at him,
But at a glance you will pick out
His high-born features from among the rest.
And see he bears himself like any courtier.
He has a noble pedigree, but he's the greatest fool of all
my household.

SOPHIA: What breeding's this, to leave me here alone!
And he my husband that's to be,
And pock-marked also is his face, I do protest.

(*The Major-Domo approaches the servants of Lerchenau most po-
litely and conducts them out of the room. At the same time
Faninal's servants withdraw—all but two, who offer wine and
comforts.*)

FANINAL (*to the Baron*):
Perhaps you would partake . . .
'Tis Tokay, an old vintage.

BARON: Good, Faninal, you know what's right and fitting
To serve a mellow wine of an old vintage to drink a
young bride's health,
You have my commendation.
(*To Octavian*).
'Tis not amiss to show some condescension
In talking to gimcrack nobility,
And show them clearly,
They must not deem themselves **equal to such as us.**

OCTAVIAN (*spitzig*):

    Ich muss deine Liebden sehr bewundern.
    Hast wahrhaft grosse Weltmanieren.
    Könntst einen Ambassadeur vorstellen heut wie morgen.

BARON (*derb*):

    Ich hol' mir jetzt das Mädl her.
    Soll uns jetzt Konversation vormachen,
    damit ich seh', wie sie beschlagen ist.
    (*Geht hinüber, nimmt Sophie bei der Hand, führt sie mit sich.*)

BARON:

    Eh bien: Nun plauder' Sie uns eins, mir und dem Vetter
                           Taverl.
    Sag' Sie heraus, auf was Sie sich halt in der Eh' am
                         meisten freut.
    (*Setzt sich, will sie halb auf seinen Schoss ziehen.*)

SOPHIE (*entzieht sich ihm*):

    Wo denkt Er hin?

BARON (*behaglich*):

    Pah! Wo ich hindenk'! Komm' Sie da ganz nah zu mir,
    dann will ich Ihr erzählen, wo ich hindenk'.
    (*Gleiches Spiel, Sophie entzieht sich ihm heftiger.*)

BARON (*behaglich*):

    Wär Ihr leicht präferabel, dass man wegen Ihrer
    den Zeremonienmeister sollt' hervortun?
    Mit „mille pardons" und „devotion"
    und „Geh da weg" und „hab' Respekt"?

SOPHIE:

    Wahrhaftig und ja gefiele mir das besser!

BARON (*lachend*):

    Mir auch nicht! Das sieht Sie! Mir auch ganz und gar
                           nicht!
    Bin einer biedern offenherzigen Galanterie recht zugetan.
    (*Er macht Anstalt, sie zu küssen, sie wehrt sich energisch.*)

FANINAL (*nachdem er Octavian den zweiten Stuhl angeboten hat, den
dieser ablehnt*):

    Wie ist mir denn! Da sitzt ein Lerchenau
    und karessiert in Ehrbarkeit mein Sopherl, als wär' sie ihm
                         schon angetraut.
    Und da steht ein Rofrano, sonsten nix —
    der Bruder vom Marchese Obersttruchsess.

OCTAVIAN (*zornig für sich*):

    Das ist ein Kerl, dem möcht' ich wo begegnen
    mit meinem Degen da,
    wo ihn kein Wächter schreien hört.
    Ja, das ist alles, was ich möcht'.

SOPHIE (*zum Baron*):

    Ei, lass Er doch, wir sind nicht so vertraut!

BARON (*zu Sophie*):

    Geniert Sie sich leicht vor dem Vetter Taverl?
    Da hat Sie unrecht.
    In der grossen Welt,
    wo doch die hohe Schul' ist für Manieren,

OCTAVIAN (*pointedly*) :

> I vow, I do admire your Lordship's wisdom.
> The great world's manners you have mastered.
> Like an Ambassador or Chancellor you bear yourself.

BARON (*roughly*) :

> I'll bring the wench now to my side.
> That I may see if her talk pleases me,

> (*Crosses over, takes Sophia by the hand and leads her back with him.*)

> That of her points and paces I may judge.
> Eh bien! Now let us hear you talk, me and you cousin
> > Tavy,
> Tell me now, what will in marriage, think you, please
> > you most?

SOPHIA (*withdrawing from him*) :

> What mean these ways?

BARON (*at his ease*) :

> Pooh! Why this pother? Now come here quite close to
> > me
> And I will tell you quickly all my meaning.
> (*Same by-play. Sophia tries to withdraw still more angrily.*)
> Would your la'ship perhaps prefer it, if one came
> Like a dancing master, bowing and congeeing,
> With "Mille Pardons" and "Devotion"
> And "By your leave" and "My respects."

SOPHIA:

> Most surely yes, 'twould please me better!

BARON:

> I thing not so—All flim-flam, fudge and silly nonsense—
> My taste is all for free and easy ways, and open-hearted
> > gallantry.
> (*He tries to kiss her. She resists energetically.*)

FANINAL (*offering a chair to Octavian, who refuses.*) :

> What! Can it be? There sits a Lerchenau
> A-paying his addresses to my Sophy, as if they had been
> > wed and all,
> And there stands a Rofrano, just as natural!
> A Count Rofrano, nothing less—
> A brother to the Empress' Lord High Steward.

OCTAVIAN:

> Faugh! What a boor! How I should like to meet him
> Alone with my good sword—
> No watch to hear him shout for help—
> Yes, nothing better I should wish.

SOPHIA (*to Baron*) :

> I pray you cease, we are but strangers yet!

BARON (*to Sophia*) :

> Is it my cousin Octavian that makes you bashful?
> That's out of reason.
> In the highest ranks
> Where surely they know most about good manners

da gibt's frei nichts,
was man nit willig pardonnieren tat',
wenn's nur mit einer adligen Noblesse
und richtigen Galanterie vollführet wird.
(Er wird immer zärtlicher, sie weiss sich kaum zu helfen.)

FANINAL *(für sich)*:
Wär' nur die Mauer da von Glas,
dass alle bürgerlichen Neidhammeln von Wien uns könnten
so en famille beisammen so sitzen sehn!
. Dafür wollt' ich mein Lerchenfelder Eckhaus geben, meiner
Seel'!

OCTAVIAN *(wütend)*:
Dass ich das Mannsbild sehen muss,
so frech, so unverschämt mit ihr.
Ich büss' all meine Sünden ab!
Könnt' ich hinaus und fort von hier!

BARON *(zu Sophie)*:
Lass Sie die Flausen nur! Gehört doch jetzo mir!
(Halb für sich, sie kajolierend.)
Ganz meine Massen! Schultern wie ein Henderl!
Geht all's recht! Sei Sie gut! Geht alles so wie am
Schnürl!
Hundsmager noch — das macht nichts, aber weiss
mit einem Glanz darauf, wie ich ihn ästimier'!
Ich hab' halt ja ein lerchenauisch Glück!

SOPHIE *(reisst sich los und stampft auf)*.

BARON *(vergnügt)*:
Ist Sie ein rechter Kapricenschädel!
(Auf und ihr nach.)
Steigt Ihr das Blut gar in die Wangen,
dass man sich die Hand verbrennt?

SOPHIE *(rot und blass von Zorn)*:
Lass Er die Hand davon!

OCTAVIAN *(in stummer Wut, verdrückt das Glas, das er in der Hand
hält, und schmeisst die Scherben zu Boden)*.

DUENNA *(läuft mit Grazie zu Octavian hinüber, hebt die Scherben auf
und raunt ihm mit Entzücken zu)*:
Ist recht ein familiärer Mann, der Herr Baron!
Man delektiert sich, was er all's für Einfäll' hat!

BARON *(dicht bei Sophie)*:
Geht mir nichts drüber!
Könnt' mich mit Schmachterei und Zärtlichkeit
nicht halb so glücklich machen, meiner Seel'!

SOPHIE *(scharf, ihm ins Gesicht)*:
Ich denk' nicht dran, dass ich Ihn glücklich mach'!

*(Indessen ist der Notar mit dem Schreiber eingetreten, eingeführt
durch Faninals Haushofmeister. Dieser meldet ihn dem Herrn
von Faninal leise; Faninal geht zum Notar nach rückwärts hin,
spricht mit ihm und sieht einen vom Schreiber vorgehaltenen
Aktenfaszikel durch.)*

There's nothing
That will not be allowed, and freely pardoned,
If but it be done rightly with a courtly grace,
Befitting folk of birth and breeding.

(The Baron grows more and more importunate—she is at her wit's end.)

FANINAL (*to himself*):

Would that the walls could be of glass . . .
If but the townsfolk all could see them sitting there,
Quite en famille, how green would they turn with envy!
Gladly for that I'd give the best of all my houses, on my
soul!

OCTAVIAN (*furious*):

Oh, that I must stand here and see him thus,
So coarse and so unmannerly.
Could I but up and flee from here!

BARON (*to Sophia*):

Put but your airs aside, for I have got you now!
All goes well! Never fear! 'Tis all just as I wish it!

(Half to himself, fondling her.)

Just as I wish it! Tender as a pullet!
Not very plump—no matter—but so white,
White—and what a bloom—there's nothing I like more!
I have the luck of all the Lerchenaus!

(Sophia tears herself away and stamps her feet.)

Gad, what a mettlesome little filly!

(Rises and runs after her.)

And see how hot her cheeks are burning—
Full hot enough to burn one's hands!

SOPHIA (*pale with anger*):

Hands off, I say! Be gone!

(Octavian in silent anger, crushes the glass he holds in his hand and throws the pieces to the ground.)

(Marianne runs with affected grace towards Octavian, picks up the pieces and confides her delight to him.)

MARIANNE: 'Tis most uncommon easy ways his Lordship has,
The jests he thinks of, la, they make me laugh till I
could cry.

(In the meantime the Attorney has entered with his clerk, introduced by Faninal's Major-Domo. He announces them in a whisper to Faninal: Faninal goes to the back to the Attorney, speaks with him and looks through a bundle of documents presented to him by the Clerk.)

SOPHIE (*zwischen den Zähnen*):

Hat nie kein Mann dergleichen Reden nicht zu mir geführt!
Möcht wissen, was ihm dünkt von mir und Ihm?
Was ist Er denn zu mir?

BARON (*gemütlich*):

Wird kommen über Nacht,
dass Sie ganz sanft
wird wissen, was ich bin zu Ihr.
Ganz wie's im Liedel heisst — kennt Sie das Liedel?
Lalalalala —

(*Recht gefühlvoll.*)

Wie ich dein alles werde sein!
Mit mir, mit mir keine Kammer dir zu klein,
ohne mich, ohne mich jeder Tag dir so bang,

(*frech und plump*)

mit mir, mit mir keine Nacht dir zu lang?

SOPHIE (*da er sie fester an sich drückt, reisst sich los und stösst ihn
heftig zurück.*)

DUENNA (*zu ihr eilend*):

Ist recht ein familiärer Mann, der Herr Baron!
Man delektiert sich, was er all's für Einfäll' hat!

(*Krampfhaft in Sophie hineinredend.*)

Nein, was er all's für Einfäll' hat, der Herr Baron!

OCTAVIAN (*ohne hinzusehen, und doch sieht er alles, was vorgeht*):

Ich steh' auf glüh'nden Kohlen!
Ich fahr' aus meiner Haut!
Ich büss' in dieser einen Stund'
all meine Sünden ab!

BARON (*für sich, sehr vergnügt*):

Wahrhaftig und ja, ich hab' halt ein lerchenauisch Glück!
Gibt gar nichts auf der Welt, was mich so enflammiert
und also vehement verjüngt als wie ein rechter Trotz!

(*Faninal und der Notar, hinter ihnen der Schreiber, sind an der
linken Seite nach vorne gekommen.*)

BARON (*sowie er den Notar erblickt, eifrig zu Sophie, ohne zu ahnen, was
in ihr vorgeht*):

Dort gibt's Geschäften jetzt, muss mich dispensieren:
bin dort von Wichtigkeit. Indessen
der Vetter Taverl leistet Ihr Gesellschaft!

FANINAL: Wenn's jetzt belieben tät', Herr Schwiegersohn!

BARON (*eifrig*):

Natürlich wird's belieben.

(*Im Vorbeigehen zum Octavian, denn er vertraulich anfasst.*)

Hab' nichts dawider,
wenn du ihr möchtest Augerln machen, Vetter,
jetzt oder künftighin.
Ist noch ein rechter Rühr-nicht-an.
Betracht's als förderlich, je mehr sie degourdiert wird.
Ist wie bei einem jungen ungerittenen **Pferd.**

SOPHIA (*with clenched teeth*) :
> There is no man has ever dared to speak to me like **this**!
> What can you think of me and of yourself?
> What are you, pray, to me?

BARON (*cententedly*) :
> One day you'll wake and find
> That you have just
> Discovered what I am to you.
> Just as the ballad says—Do you not know it?
> La la la la la.
>> (*Very sentimentally.*)
> How to you I'll be all in all!
> With me, with me there's no attic seems too small.
> Without me, without me slowly will pass all the days,
>> (*Impudently and coarsely.*)
> With me, with me time will seem short always!

(*Sophia, as he tries to draw her still closer to him, frees herself and violently pushes him back.*)

MARIANNE (*now hurrying to Sophia*) :
> 'Tis most uncommon easy ways his Lordship has,
> The jests he thinks of make me laugh till I could cry;
>> (*Speaking to Sophia with feverish energy.*)
> They make me laugh till I could cry, his Lordship's jests.

OCTAVIAN (*without looking at the Baron, and yet aware of all that is passing*) :
> On coals of fire I'm standing!
> 'Tis more than I can bear!
> In this one hour 'fore Heav'n I do
> Penance for all my sins!

BARON (*to himself, very contented*) :
> I always did say, I have all the luck of all the
>> Lerchenaus!
> Nothing else in the world does so renew my youth
> Or whet my appetite so well as a real spitfire can.

(*Faninal and the Attorney, followed by the Clerk, have advanced to the front, on the left.*)

BARON (*as soon as he sees the Attorney, eagerly to Sophia, without the smallest idea what she is thinking*) :
> But now there's work to do, so for a while forgive me:
> They need my presence there. And meanwhile
> There's Cousin Tavy, he will entertain you!

FANINAL : May I beg the honour now, dear Son-in-law!

BARON (*eagerly*) :
> Of course you'll have the honour.
>> (*In passing to Octavian, whom he touches familiarly.*)
> 'Twould not displease me
> If you should cast some sheep's eyes at her, Cousin,
> Now or at any time:
> You're still content with looks alone.
> The more she learns from you, the better I shall like it
> For a girl, do you see, is just like an unbroken foal:

Kommt all's dem Angetrauten letzterdings zugut',
wofern er sein eh'lich Privilegium
zunutz zu machen weiss.

(*Er geht nach links. Der Diener, der den Notar einliess, hat indessen die Türe links geöffnet. Faninal und der Notar schicken sich an, hineinzugehen. Der Baron misst Faninal mit dem Blick und bedeutet ihm, drei Schritte Distanz zu nehmen. Faninal tritt devot zurück. Der Baron nimmt den Vortritt, vergewissert sich, dass Faninal drei Schritte Abstand hat und geht gravitätisch durch die Tür links ab. Faninal hinter ihm, dann der Notar, dann der Schreiber. Der Bediente schliesst die Türe links und geht ab, lässt aber die Flügeltüre nach dem Vorsaal offen. Der servierende Diener ist schon früher abgegangen.*)

SOPHIE (*rechts, steht verwirrt und beschämt*).

DUENNA (*neben ihr knickst nach der Türe hin, bis sie sich schliesst*).

OCTAVIAN (*mit einem Blick hinter sich, gewiss zu sein, dass die anderen abgegangen sind, tritt schnell zu Sophie hinüber, bebend vor Aufregung*):
Wird Sie das Mannsbild da heiraten, ma cousine?

SOPHIE (*einen Schritt auf ihr zu, leise*):
Nicht um die Welt!
(*Mit einem Blick auf die Duenna.*)
Mein Gott, wär' ich allein mit Ihm,
dass ich Ihn bitten könnt'! dass ich Ihn bitten könnt'!

OCTAVIAN (*halblaut, schnell*):
Was ist's, das Sie mich bitten möcht'? Sag' Sie mir's
schnell!

SOPHIE (*noch einen Schritt näher zu ihm*):
O mein Gott, dass Er mir halt hilft! Und Er wird mir nicht
helfen wollen,
weil Er halt sein Vetter ist!

OCTAVIAN (*heftig*):
Nenn' ihn Vetter aus Höflichkeit;
Gott sei Lob und Dank,
hab' ihn im Leben vor dem gestrigen Tag nie gesehn!

(*Quer durch den Vorsaal flüchten einige von den Mädgen des Hauses, denen die Lerchenauschen Bedienten auf den Fersen sind. Der Leiblakai und der mit dem Pflaster auf der Nase jagen einem hübschen jungen Mädchen nach und bringen sie fast an der Schwelle zum Salon bedenklich in die Enge.*)

DER FANINALSCHE HAUSHOFMEISTER (*kommt verstört hereingelaufen, die Duenna zu Hilfe zu holen*):
Die Lerchenauischen sind voller Branntwein gesoffen
und gehn aufs Gesindel los zwanzigmal ärger
als Türken und Krowaten!

MARIANNE: Hol' Er unsere Leut', wo sind denn die?
(*Läuft ab mit dem Haushofmeister, sie entreissen den beiden Zudringlichen ihre Beute und führen das Mädchen ab; alles verliert sich, der Vorsaal bleibt leer.*)

70

The husband in the end gets all the benefit,
Provided he has but sense enough to use
His opportunities.

*(He goes to the left. The servant who had admitted the Attorney,
has in the meantime opened the door on the left. Faninal and
the Notary make for the door. The Baron fixes his eyes on
Faninal and signifies to him he must keep a distance of three
paces. Faninal obsequiously retreats. The Baron takes precedence, assures himself that Faninal is three paces behind him,
and walks solemnly through the door on the left. Faninal follows, and after him come the Attorney and his Clerk. The
Footman closes the door to the left, and goes out, leaving the
door which leads to the ante-room open. The Footman who was
serving refreshments has already left the room.)*

*(Sophia on the right, stands confused and humiliated. The Duenna
curtseys in the direction of the door till it closes.)*

*(Octavian, quivering with excitement, hurries towards Sophia, after
glancing backwards so as to be sure that the others have gone.)*

OCTAVIAN: And do you marry that thing there, ma Cousine?

SOPHIA *(moving one step towards him, in a whisper)*:
Not for the world!

> *(With a look to the Duenna.)*
Oh Heav'n! Could we but be alone,
That I might beg of you! That I might beg of you!

OCTAVIAN *(quickly below his breath)*:
What is it you would beg of me? Tell me now, quick!

SOPHIA *(coming another step nearer to him)*:
O, gracious Heav'n, befriend me in my need! But since
> he is your friend and cousin,
You will not wish to succour me!

OCTAVIAN *(vehemently)*:
I am his cousin but by courtesy;
Thanks be to all my stars,
I had not ever seen his hateful face till yesterday!

*(Some of the servant girls rush headlong across the anteroom,
hotly pursued by Lerchenau's attendants. The Body Servant
and the one with the plaster on his nose are at the heels of a
pretty young girl and bring her to bay close to the door of the
salon.)*

*(Faninal's Major-Domo runs in much perturbed, to call the Duenna
to help him.)*

MAJOR-DOMO: The Baron's men-folk, with our good wine quite
> besotted;
Run after all the girls, worse than an army
From Turkey, or Croatians!

MARIANNE: Fetch our men, quick, to help you. Where can they be
> hid?

*(She runs off with the Major-Domo. They rescue the girl from her
assailants and lead her away. All disappear. The anteroom
remains empty.)*

71

SOPHIE (*nun, da sie unbeobachtet ist, mit freier Stimme*):
Zu Ihm hätt' ich ein Zutrau'n, mon cousin,
so wie zu niemand auf der Welt,
dass Er mir könnte helfen,
wenn Er nur den guten Willen hätt'!

OCTAVIAN: Erst muss Sie sich selber helfen,
dann hilf ich Ihr auch.
Tu' Sie das Erste für mich,
dann tu' ich was für Sie!

SOPHIE (*zutraulich, fast zärtlich*):
Was ist denn das, was ich zuerst tun muss?

OCTAVIAN (*leise*):
Das wird Sie wohl wissen!

SOPHIE (*den Blickt unverwandt auf ihn*):
Und was ist das, was Er für mich will tun?
O sag' Er mir's!

OCTAVIAN (*entschlossen*):
Nun muss Sie ganz alleinig für uns zwei einstehn!

SOPHIE: Wie? Für uns zwei?
O sag Er's noch einmal.

OCTAVIAN (*leise*):
Für uns zwei!

SOPHIE (*mit hingegebenem Entzücken*):
Ich hab' im Leben so was Schönes nicht gehört!

OCTAVIAN (*stärker*):
Für sich und mich muss Sie sich wehren
und bleiben — was Sie ist.

SOPHIE (*nimmt seine Hand, er küsst sie schnell auf den Mund*).

OCTAVIAN (*indem er sie, die sich an ihn schmiegt, in den Armen hält
zärtlich*):
Mit Ihren Augen voller Tränen
kommt Sie zu mir, damit Sie sich beklagt.
Vor Angst muss Sie an mich sich lehnen,
Ihr armes Herz ist ganz verzagt.
Und ich muss jetzt als Ihren Freund mich zeigen
und weiss noch gar nicht, wie!
Mir ist so selig, so eigen,
dass ich dich halten darf;
Gib antwort, aber gib sie nur mit Schweigen:
Bist du von selber so zu mir gekommen?
Ja oder nein? Ja oder nein?
Du musst es nicht mit Worten sagen —
Hast du es gern getan?
Sag', oder nur aus Not?
Aus Not so alles zu mir hergetragen,
dein Herz, dein liebliches Gesicht?
Sag', ist dir nicht, dass irgendwo
in irgendeinem schönen Traum
das einmal schon so war?
Spürst du's wie ich?
Sag', spürst du's so wie ich?

SOPHIA (*speaking freely, now that they are unobserved*):
> In you I place my trust, in you, mon Cousin,
> Knowing that you, like no one else,
> Could be my help, my saviour,
> Would you but bend your will to it!

OCTAVIAN:
> First must you for yourself take courage,
> Then I too will help.
> Till you have helped yourself,
> I can do naught for you!

SOPHIA (*confidingly, almost tenderly*):
> What is it then, I for myself must do?

OCTAVIAN (*softly*):
> Surely you know it!

SOPHIA (*looking at him undismayed*):
> And what is it that you will do for me,
> Now tell me that!

OCTAVIAN (*decidedly*):
> Now must you strike a blow alone—you for us twain!

SOPHIA:
> What, for us twain?
> O say it once again!

OCTAVIAN (*softly*):
> For us twain!

SOPHIA (*rapturously*):
> O words of rapture! Naught so sweet till now I heard.

OCTAVIAN (*loudly*):
> To save us both must you be steadfast,
> And still be—

SOPHIA: Still be?

OCTAVIAN: What you are.

(*Sophia seizes his hand, bends over it, kisses it quickly before he can withdraw it. He kisses her on the lips.*)

OCTAVIAN (*holding her in his arms as she nestles closely to him*):
> With tear-dimmed eyes, all affrighted,
> My aid you seek, telling your sorrows all,
> Fear naught, henceforth to me united,
> Fear naught, whatever may befall!
> To save you now must be my one endeavour,
> And yet I know not how.
> Rapture like this did ye never
> Grant to a mortal, ye gods!
> Give me answer, but with eloquent silence,—
> Did your free will to me thus guide you hither?
> Say yea or nay—say yea or nay!
> No words could tell me all your meaning.
> Was your free will your guide?
> Say, or your direful need?
> Why brought you here these gifts so lavish?
> Your loving heart, your face so fair?
> Say, seems it not that once in days
> Far off, in some dear magic dream
> We loved each other thus?
> Think you not so?
> Dream'd you never thus, as I?
> My heart, my soul,
> Will aye be with you?
> Wheresoe'er you be,
> For all eternity.

SOPHIE: Ich möchte mich bei Ihm verstecken
und nichts mehr wissen von der Welt.
Wenn Er mich so in Seinen Armen hält,
kann mich nichts Hässliche erschrecken.
Da bleiben möcht' ich, da!
Und schweigen, und was mir auch gescheh',
geborgen wie der Vogel in den Zweigen,
stillstehn und spüren: Er ist in der Näh'!
Mir müsste angst und bang im Herzen sein
statt dessen fühl' ich Freud und Seligkeit
und keine Pein,
ich könnt' es nicht mit Worten sagen!
Hab' ich was Unrechtes getan?
Ich war halt in der Not!
Da war Er mir nah!
Da war es Sein Gesicht,
Sein' Augen jung und licht,
auf das ich mich gericht',
Sein liebes Gesicht —
Er muss mir Seinen Schutz vergonnen,
Was Er will, werd' ich können;
Bleib' Er nur bei mir!
Er muss mir Seinen Schutz vergönnen —
Bleib Er nur bei mir!

*(Aus den Kaminen in den rückwärtigen Ecken sind links Valzacchi,
rechts Annina lautlos spähend herausgeglitten. Lautlos schleichen
sie, langsam, auf den Zehen, näher. Octavian zieht Sophie an
sich, küsst sie auf den Mund; in diesem Augenblick sind die
Italiener dicht hinter ihnen, ducken sich hinter den Lehnsesseln;
jetzt springen sie vor, Annina packt Sophie, Valzacchi fasst
Octavian.)*

VALZACCHI und ANNINA (*zu zweien schreiend*):

Herr Baron von Lerchenau! — Herr Baron von Lerchenau! —

OCTAVIAN (*springt zur Seite nach links*).

VALZACCHI (*der Mühe hat, ihn zu halten, atemlos zu Annina*):

Lauf und 'ole Seine Gnade!
Snell, nur snell, ik muss 'alten diese 'err!

ANNINA: Lass ich die Fräulein aus, läuft sie mir weg!

ZU ZWEIEN: Herr Baron von Lerchenau,
Herr Baron von Lerchenau!
Komm' zu sehn die Fräulein Braut!
Mit eine junge Kavalier!
Kommen eilig, kommen hier! Ecco!

*(Baron tritt aus der Tür links. Die Italiener lassen ihre Opfer los,
springen zur Seite, verneigen sich vor dem Baron mit vielsagender
Gebärde.)*

SOPHIE (*schmiegt sich ängstlich an Octavian*).

SOPHIA: What rapture, thus with you to hide me
            And hear no whisper of the world,
            When thus contented in your arms I lie,
            I fear naught, ill can ne'er betide me.
            There fain I'd linger, there, for ever
            Secure from grief and fear,
            And know that our fond union naught can sever.
            Naught now can harm me,
            You, you are always near.
            My pulse should cease to beat for shame and dread.
            But lo! I feel an endless joy and happiness.
            All pain is fled,
            No words can tell you all my meaning,
            Haply 'twas sinful what I did?
            But direful was my need,
            And lo! you were near—
            I saw your face so fair—
            Your eyes, your valiant air—
            And healed was my despair.
            And thenceforth nothing I know,
            Nothing more of myself—
            O stay now with me—
            Protect me, save me, stay beside me,
            I follow wheresoe'er you guide me.
            Save me, leave me not—

(From the fireplaces to the left and right respectively come Valzacchi and Annina noiselessly and watch the lovers. They approach silently on tiptoe. Octavian draws Sophia to him and kisses her on the lips. At this moment the two Italians are close behind them. They duck behind the armchairs. Then they jump forward, Annina seizes Sophia, Valzacchi takes hold of Octavian.)

VALZACCHI and ANNINA *(screaming together)*:
            Quick, Baron Lerchenau, quick, Baron Lerchenau!

                    (Octavian leaps aside to the right.)

VALZACCHI *(holding him with difficulty, breathless to Annina)*:
            Run, bring 'izzer 'is Lords'ip—
            Quick, make 'aste: I must 'old zis young man.

ANNINA: If I not 'old zis lady, she escape me!

VALZACCHI and ANNINA: Quick! Baron Lerchenau!
            Quick! Baron Lerchenau!
            Come to see your future wife
            Discovered viz a gentleman,
            Pray come quickly! Pray come 'ere!

(The Baron enters through the door on the left and with folded arms contemplates the group. Ominous pause. Sophia nestles timidly close to Octavian.)

                                        Ecco!

75

BARON (*die Arme über die Brust gekreuzt, betrachtet sich die Gruppe.*
Unheilsschwangere Pause, endlich):
Eh bien, Mamsell, was hat Sie mir zu sagen?

SOPHIE (*schweigt*).

BARON (*der durchaus nicht ausser Fassung ist*):
Nun, resolvier' Sie sich!

SOPHIE:
Mein Gott, was soll ich sagen,
Er wird mich nicht verstehn!

BARON (*gemütlich*):
Das werden wir ja sehn!

OCTAVIAN (*einen Schritt auf den Baron zu*):
Eu'r Liebden muss ich halt vermelden,
dass sich in Seiner Angelenheit
was Wichtiges verändert hat!

BARON (*gemütlich*):
Verändert? Ei, nicht dass ich wüsst'!

OCTAVIAN:
Darum soll Er es jetzt erfahren!
Die Fräulein —

BARON:
Ei, Er ist nicht faul! Er weiss zu profitieren,
mit Seine siebzehn Jahr'! Ich muss Ihm gratulieren!

BARON (*halb zu sich*):
Ist mir ordentlich, ich seh' mich selber!
Muss lachen über den Filou, den pudeljungen.

OCTAVIAN: Die Fräulein —

BARON: Ei! Sie ist wohl stumm und hat Ihn angestellt für Ihren
Advokaten!

OCTAVIAN: Die Fräulein —
(*Er hält abermals inne, wie um Sophie sprechen zu lassen.*)
SOPHIE (*angstvoll*):
Nein! Nein! Nein! Ich bring' den Mund nicht auf.
Sprech' Er für mich!

OCTAVIAN (*entschlossen*):
Die Fräulein —

BARON (*ihm nachstotternd*):
Die Fräulein, die Fräulein! Die Fräulein! Die Fräulein!
Ist eine Kreuzerkomödi wahrhaftig!
Jetzt echappier' Er sich, sonst reisst mir die Geduld.

OCTAVIAN (*sehr bestimmt*):
Die Fräulein, kurz und gut,
die Fräulein mag Ihn nicht.

BARON (*gemütlich*):
Sei Er da ausser Sorg'. Wird schon lernen mich mögen.
(*Auf Sophie zu.*)
Komm' Sie da jetzt hinein: wird gleich an Ihrer sein,
die Unterschrift zu geben.

SOPHIE (*zurücktretend*):
Um keinen Preis geh' ich an seiner Hand hinein!
Wie kann ein Kavalier so ohne Zartheit sein!

BARON: Eh bien, Ma'mselle! What would you wish to tell me?
              (*Sophia remains silent. The Baron retains his composure.*)
              Well, do not hesitate.

SOPHIA: Alas! What could I tell you? You would not under-
                                                          stand—

BARON (*quickly*):
              Ecod, I think I will.

OCTAVIAN (*moving a step nearer the Baron*):
              'Tis my duty to inform your Lordship
              That most important changes have been wrought
              In matters that concern you nearly.

BARON (*genially*):
              Important? Changed? Not that I know!

OCTAVIAN: And therefore I now have to tell you,
              This lady—

BARON: Well, you lose no time,
              And take the best advantage
              For all your seventeen years—I must congratulate you!

OCTAVIAN: This lady—

BARON: 'Gad, I like you well. Was I not just so?
              The rascal! I must laugh, egad!
              To start so early?

OCTAVIAN: This lady—

BARON: Ah! She's dumb, I presume, and is employing you
              To plead as her attorney.

OCTAVIAN: This lady— — —
                            (*He pauses again, as though to let Sophia speak.*)

SOPHIA (*timidly*):
              No, no! I cannot speak the word—
              Speak you for me—

OCTAVIAN (*with determination*):
              This lady—

BARON (*mimicking him*):
              This lady, this lady, this lady, this lady!
              This is jack-pudding foolery, by heaven!
              And you had best depart, I've borne with you too long.

OCTAVIAN (*very determined*):
              This lady, once for all now, will have none of you.

BARON: As for that, have no fear—She will soon enough have
                                                          me.
                            (*To Sophia*):
              Come with me now in there— you will be needed soon to
                                         sign the marriage contract.

SOPHIA (*retreating*):
              No, not for all the world I'll let you lead me in!
              How can a gentleman be so indelicate!

77

OCTAVIAN (*der jetzt zwischen den beiden anderen und der Tür links*) :
　　Versteht Er deutsch?　Die Fräulein hat sich resolviert.
　　Sie will Euer Gnaden ungeheirat' lassen
　　in Zeit und Ewigkeit!

BARON (*mit der Miene eines Mannes, der es eilig hat*) :
　　Mancari!　Jungfernred' ist nicht gehaun und nicht ge-
　　　　　　　　　　　　　　　　　　　　　　　stochen!
　　Verlaub' Sie jetzt!

　　　　　　　　　　　　　　　(*Nimmt sie bei der Hand.*)
　　(*Er macht Miene, Sophie mit scheinbarer Unbefangenheit gegen die
　　Mitteltür zu führen, nachdem ihm die Italiener lebhafte Zeichen
　　gegeben haben, diesen Weg zu nehmen.*)
　　Komm' Sie!　Gehn zum Herrn Vater dort hinüber!
　　Ist bereits der nähere Weg!

OCTAVIAN (*ihm nach, dicht an ihr*) :
　　Ich hoff', er kommt vielmehr jetzt mit mir hinters Haus,
　　ist dort recht ein bequemer Garten.

BARON (*setzt so'nen Weg fort, mit gespielter Unbefangenheit Sophie an
　　der Hand nach jener Richtung zu führen bestrebt, über die
　　Schulter zurück*) :
　　Bewahre.　Wär' mir jetzo nicht genehm.
　　Lass um all's den Notari nicht warten.
　　Wär' gar ein Affront für die Jungfer Braut!

OCTAVIAN (*fasst ihn an Aermel*) :
　　Beim Satan, Er hat eine dicke Haut!
　　Auch dort die Tür passiert Er mir nicht!
　　Ich schrei's Ihm jetzt in Sein Gesicht:
　　Ich schrei's Ihn für einen Filou,
　　einen Mitgiftjäger,
　　einen durchtriebenen Lügner und schmutzigen Bauer,
　　einen Kerl ohne Anstand und Ehr'!
　　Und wenn's sein muss, geb' ich ihm auf dem Fleck die
　　　　　　　　　　　　　　　　　　　　　　　Lehr'!

SOPHIE (*hat sich vom Baron losgerissen und ist hinter Octavian zurück-
　　gesprungen.　Sie stehen links, ziemlich vor der Tür*).

BARON (*steckt zwei Finger in den Mund und tut einen gellenden Pfiff.
　　Dann*) :
　　Was so ein Bub' in Wien mit siebzehn Jahr
　　schon für ein vorlaut Mundwerk hat!

　　　　　　　　　(*Er sieht sich nach der Mitteltür um.*)
　　Doch Gott sei Lob, mann kennt in hiesiger Stadt
　　den Mann, der vor ihm steht,
　　halt bis hinauf zu kaiserlicher Majestät!
　　Man ist halt was man ist, und braucht's nicht zu beweisen.
　　Das lass Er sich gesagt sein und geb' mir den Weg da frei.

(*Die Lerchenausche Livree ist vollzählig in der Mitteltür aufmar-
　schiert; er vergewissert sich dessen durch einen Blick nach rück-
　wärts.　Er rückt jetzt gegen die beiden vor, entschlossen, sich
　Sophiens und des Ausgangs zu bemächtigen.*)
　　Wär mir wahrhaftig leid, wenn meine Leut' da hinten —

OCTAVIAN (*who has now taken his place between th.m and the door on the left*):

Please understand. The lady has determined finally
That she will let your Lordship stay unmarried
For now and evermore!

BARON:

Baby-talk! By hard words ne'er a bone is broken!
And time is short.

(*Takes her by the hand.*)

(*He attempts, with feigned unconcern, to lead Sophia towards the centre door, after the Italians have signified to him by lively gestures to take that way.*)

Come, now! Go to your father, who awaits us.
By this door is the speedier way.

OCTAVIAN (*following them, close to her*):

I beg you rather come with me—
At the back of the house
I know a most convenient garden.

(*The Baron continues in the same direction still with simulated unconcern, trying to lead away Sophia, whom he still holds by the hand, and speaks over his shoulder.*)

BARON:

Enough of this. Your jests are most ill-timed—
We must not keep the Notary waiting,
'Twould be an insult to this lady here.

OCTAVIAN (*seizing him by the sleeve*):

By heaven! I never knew so tough a hide!
And by this door I swear you will not pass—
That you may know it, to your face
I saw that you are but a cheat,
And dowry-hunter,
Naught but a rascally, lying, unmannerly clown, Sir,
But a boor, unclean in thought and in deed,
And with my sword I'll give you the sharp lesson you
        need.

(*Sophia has freed herself from the Baron and takes refuge behind Octavian. They stand to the left, almost in front of the door.*)

BARON (*putting two fingers into his mouth and giving a shrill whistle*):

How soon these boys do learn in Vienna here,
To set their tongues a-wagging.

(*Looking towards the centre door.*)

But, heav'n be praised, the Court and all the Town
Know him that you affront,
E'en to the throne of Her Imperial Majesty!
We all are what we are, and there's no need to prove it.
Now, young Sir, I have said my say, and get you from
        my path—

(*Lerchenau's servants, in full numbers, have appeared at the centre door. The Baron, by a backward glance, assures himself of their presence. He now approaches Sophia and Octavian, determined to secure Sophia and his retreat.*)

Truly I should regret it if my people yonder—

OCTAVIAN (*wütend*):
Ah, untersteht Er sich, Seine Bedienten
hineinzumischen in unsern Streit!
Jetzt zieh Er oder gnad' ihm Gott!

(*Er zieht.*)
(*Die Lerchenauschen, die schon einige Schritte vorgerückt waren,
werden durch diesen Anblick einigermassen unschlüssig und
stellen ihren Vormarsch ein.*)

BARON (*tut einen Schritt, sich Sophiens zu bemächtigen*):

OCTAVIAN (*schreit ihn an*):
Zum Satan, zieh' Er oder ich stech' Ihn nieder!

SOPHIE: O Gott, was wird denn jetzt geschehn?

BARON (*retiriert etwas*):
Vor einer Dame, pfui! So sei Er doch gescheit!

OCTAVIAN (*fährt wütend auf ihn los*).

BARON (*zieht, fällt ungeschickt aus und hat schon die Spitze von Octavians Degen im Oberarm. Die Lerchenauschen stürzen vor*).

BARON (*indem er den Degen fallen lässt*).
Mord! Mord! Mein Blut! Zu Hilfe! Mörder! Mörder!
Mörder!

(*Die Diener stürzen alle zugleich auf Octavian los. Dieser springt
nach rechts hinüber und hält sie sich vom Leib, indem er seinen
Degen blitzschnell um sich kreisen lässt. Der Almosenier, Valzacchi und Annina eilen auf den Baron zu, den sie stützen und
auf einem der Stühle in der Mitte niederlassen.*)

BARON (*von ihnen umgeben und dem Publikum verstellt*):
Ich hab' ein hitzig' Blut! Um Aerzt', um Leinwand!
Verband her! Ich verblut' mich auf eins, zwei!
Aufhalten den! Um Polizei! Um Polizei!

DIE LERCHENAUSCHEN (*indem sie mit mehr Ostentation als Entschlossen-
heit auf Octavian eindringen*):
Spinnweb' her! Feuerschwamm!
Reisst's ihn den Spadi weg!
Schlagt's ihn tot auf'm Fleck!

(*Die sämtliche Faninalsche Dienerschaft, auch das weibliche Haus-
gesinde, Küchenpersonal, Stallpagen sind zur Mitteltür herein-
geströmt.*)
(*Valzacchi und der Almosenier ziehen dem Baron, der fortwährend
stöhnt, seinen Rock aus.*)

DIE FANINALISCHE DIENERSCHAFT:
Schaut's nur die Fräulein an,
Schaut's, wie sie blass is'!

OCTAVIAN (*Sophie verzweifelt zurufend*):
Liebste!

(*Die Lerchenauschen machen Miene, sich zu diesem Zweck der
Hemden der jüngeren und hübscheren Mägde zu bemächtigen.
Handgemenge, bis Faninal beginnt. In diesem Augenblick kommt
die Duenna, die fortgestürzt war, zurück, atemlos, beladen mit
Leinwand; hinter ihr zwei Mägde mit Schwamm und Wasser-*

OCTAVIAN :   Now, as you prize your life, Sir, do not dare
                To drag your grooms and lackeys into our quarrel.
                Draw, Sir, or Heav'n protect your soul!

(The Baron's servants, who had already approached a few steps, hesitate as they see what is happening and pause in their advance. The Baron takes a step forward in order to secure Sophia.)

                Draw, ruffian, draw! Or on my sword I'll split you.

SOPHIA :   Oh! Heaven! Oh, what will happen now!

BARON *(withdraws a step)* :
                What! In a lady's presence! Is the boy possessed?

(Octavian rushes at him furiously, the Baron draws and lunging clumsily receives the point of Octavian's sword in his upper arm. Lerchenau's servants rush forward.)

BARON *(dropping his sword)* :
                Help! Help! I bleed! A surgeon! Murder! Murder!
                                        Murder!

(All the servants rush towards Octavian. He springs to the right and keeps them at arm's length whirling his sword about him. The Almoner, Valzacchi and Annina hurry to the Baron, and supporting him, lead him to one of the chairs in the middle of the room.)

BARON *(surrounded by his servants and the Italians, who conceal him from the public.)*
                I have most fiery blood! A doctor! Linen!
                A bandage! Call the watch! I bleed to death ere you
                                  count three!
                Don't let him go! And call the watch! And call the
                                    watch!

LERCHENAU'S SERVANTS *(closing round Octavian with more swagger than courage)* :
                Break his crown!
                Cobwebs here! Sponge him down!
                Take his sword, break his head
                Who's afraid? Kill him dead!

(All Faninal's Servants, the female domestics, the kitchen staff and the stable hands, have streamed in by the centre door.)

(Valzacchi and the Almoner divest the Baron, who groans uninterruptedly, of his coat.)

FANINAL'S SERVANTS : Look at the brazen thing,
                How dared she do it?

OCTAVIAN *(calling to Sophia, in despair)* :
                Dearest!

(Lerchenau's Servants make as if to tear up the clothes of the younger and prettier servant maids. Mêlée till Faninal comes At this moment the Duenna, who had rushed out, returns, breathless, bringing linen for bandages, behind her two maids with sponges and basins. They surround the Baron and busy themselves about him. Faninal rushes in by the door to the

becken. Sie umgeben den Baron mit eifriger Hilfeleistung.
Faninal kommt zur Türe links hereingestürzt, hinter ihm der
Notar und der Schreiber, die in der Türe ängstlich stehen bleiben.)

BARON (*man hört seine Stimme, ohne viel von ihm zu sehen*):
    Ich kann ein jedes Blut mit Ruhe fliessen sehen,
    nur bloss das meinig' nicht! Oh! Oh!
                    (*Die Duenna anschreiend.*)
    So tu' Sie doch was G'scheidt's, so rett' Sie doch mein
                              Leben!
    Oh! Oh!

(*Sophie ist, wie sie ihres Vaters ansichtig wird, nach rechts vorne*
hingelaufen, steht neben Octavian, der nun seinen Degen ein-
steckt).

ANNINA (*knicksend und eifrig zu Faninal links vorne*):
    Der junge Kavalier
    und die Fräulein Braut, Gnaden,
    waren im Geheimen
    schon recht vertraut, Gnaden!
    Wir voller Eifer
    für'n Herrn Baron, Gnaden,
    haben sie betreten
    in aller Devotion, Gnaden!

DUENNA (*um den Baron beschäftigt*):
    So ein fescher Herr! So ein gross' Malheur,
    so ein schwerer Schlag, so ein Unglückstag!

FANINAL (*anfangs sprachlos, schlägt nun die Hände überm Kopf zusam-*
men und bricht aus):
    Herr Schwiegersohn! Wie ist Ihm denn? mein Herr und
                            Heiland!
    Dass Ihm in mein' Palais das hat passieren müssen!
    Gelaufen um den Medikus! Geflogen!
    Meine zehn teuren Pferd' zu Tod gehetzt!
    Ja hat denn niemand von meiner Livree
    dazwischen fahren mögen! Füttr' ich dafür
    ein Schock baumlanger Lackeln, dass mir solche Schand'
    passieren mus in meinem neuchen Stadtpalais!
                      (*Gegen Octavian hin.*)

FANINAL: Wär wohl von Euer Liebden
    hochgräfliche Gegenwart allhier
    Warhaftig einer anderen Freud' gewärtig!

OCTAVIAN (*höflich*):
    Er muss mich pardonieren
    Bin ausser Massen sehr betrübt über den Vorfall.
    Bin aber ausser Schuld. Zu einer mehr gelegenen Zeit
    erfahren Euer Liebden wohl den Hergang
    aus Ihrer Fräulein Tochter Mund.

FANINAL (*sich mühsam beherrschend*):
    Da möcht' ich recht sehr bitten!

left, followed by the Attorney and his Clerk, **who remain stand-**
ing, in great alarm, in the doorway.)

BARON (*his voice is heard, but he is scarcely visible*):
> I can look on other people's blood unmoved,
> But my own makes me faint.
> Oh! Oh!
>
> > (*Shouting to the Duenna.*)
>
> Stop whining! Stir yourself! Don't stand and watch
> His lifeless corpse will be your bridegroom!
>
> > me dying!
>
> Oh! Oh!

(*Sophia, as soon as she has seen her father, has run across the front
of the stage to the right, and stands by Octavian, who sheaths
his sword.*)

ANNINA (*curtseying and crossing over to Faninal, eagerly*):
> Ze gentleman 'ere
> And Mistress Sophia zere, yes, Sir,
> Secretly were intimate,
> I declare, yes Sir,
> Ve, full of zeal
> For his Lords'ip's sake, yes Sir,
> Kept a watch and found zem,
> And zere was no mistake, yes Sir.

MARIANNE (*busied about the Baron*):
> Such a high-born Lord!
> Such a cruel sword!
> Such a heavy blow!
> Such a day of woe!

FANINAL (*at first speechless, wrings his hands and breaks out*):
> Dear Son-in-law, how is't with you? The Saints pre-
> > serve us!
> That such a brawling boy should so disgrace my Palace!
> Send some one for a surgeon, quick! Delay not!
> Ride all my costly thoroughbreds to death.
> How is it none of my men had the sense,
> To interfere between them? Do I feed whole troops
> Of long-legged good-for-nothings, just that such dis-
> > grace
> Should fall on me in my new Palace here in Town?
> > (*Going to Octavian, with suppressed fury.*)
> Indeed from your Lordship.
> I ventured to expect for other pleasures.

OCTAVIAN (*courteously*):
> I beg you, Sir, forgive me;
> I too am grieved beyond all measure for this accident;
> But I am free from blame. At some more fitting time
> > and place
> Your Lordship from your daughter will discover
> How these mischances came to pass.

FANINAL (*controlling himself with difficulty*):
> 'Twould please me— nothing better.

83

SOPHIE (*entschlossen*):
> Wie Sie befehlen, Vater. Werd' Ihnen alles sagen.
> Der Herr dort hat sich nich so, wie er sollt', betragen.

FANINAL (*zornig*):
> Ei, von wem red't Sie da? Von Ihrem Herrn Zukünft'gen?
> Ich will nicht hoffen, wär' mir keine Manier.

SOPHIE (*ruhig*):
> Ist nicht der Fall. Seh' ihn mit nichten an dafür.
> (*Der Arzt kommt, wird sogleich zum Baron geführt.*)

FANINAL (*immer zorniger*):
> Sieht ihn nicht an?

SOPHIE:
> Nicht mehr. Bitt' Sie dafür um gnädigen Pardon.

FANINAL (*zuerst dumpf vor sich hin, dann in helle Wut ausbrechend*)
> Sieht ihn nicht an. Nicht mehr. Mich um Pardon.
> Liegt dort gestochen. Steht bei ihr. Der Junge.
> > (*Ausbrechend.*)
> Blamage. Mir auseinander meine Eh',
> Alle Neidhammeln von der Wieden und der Leimgrub'n
> auf! in der Höh! Der Medikus! Stirbt mir womöglich.
> > (*Auf Sophie zu, in höchster Wut.*)
> Sie heirat' ihn!

(*Auf Octavian, indem der Respekt vor dem Grafen Rofrano seine Grobheit zu einer knirschenden Höflichkeit herabdämpft*):
> Möchte Euer Liebden recht in aller Devotion
> gebeten haben, schleunig sich von hier zu retirieren
> und nimmer wieder zu erscheinen!
> > (*Zu Sophie.*)
> Hör Sie mich!
> Sie heirat' ihn! Und wenn er sich verbluten tät',
> so heirat' Sie ihn als Toter!

(*Der Arzt zeigt durch eine beruhigende Gebärde, dass der Verwundete sich in keiner Gefahr befindet. Octavian sucht nach seinem Hut, der unter die Füsse der Dienerschaft geraten war. Eine Magd überreicht ihm knicksend den Hut. Faninal macht Octavian eine Verbeugung, übertrieben höflich, aber unzweideutig. Octavian muss wohl gehen, möchte aber gar zu gerne Sophie noch ein Wort sagen. Er erwidert zunächst Faninals Verbeugung durch ein gleich tiefes Kompliment.*)

SOPHIE (*beeilt sich das Folgende noch zu sagen, solange Octavian es hören kann. Mit einer Reverenz*):
> Heirat' den Herrn dort nicht lebendig und nicht tot!
> Sperr' mich zuvor in meine Kammer ein!

FANINAL (*in Wut, und nachdem er abermals eine wütende Verbeugung gegen Octavian gemacht hat, die Octavian prompt erwidert*):
> Ah! Sperrst dich ein. Sind Leut' genug im Haus,
> die dich in Wagen tragen werden.

SOPHIE (*mit einem neuen Knicks*):
> Spring' aus dem Wagen noch, der mich zur Kirch'n führt!

SOPHIA (*determined*):

As you command me, father, I will relate all truly:
His Lordship did not treat me as a man of honour.

FANINAL (*angrily*):

What? Of whom do you speak? Of my future son-in-
law?
I hope 'tis not so: I should think it a sin—

SOPHIA (*quietly*):

Nay, 'tis not so—I do not look on him as such.

FANINAL (*still more angry*):

What? Not as such?

SOPHIA: No more.—I ask your gracious pardon, if I err.

(*The Doctor arrives and at once goes to the Baron.*)

FANINAL (*at first muttering to himself*):

Looks not on him? No more? Pardon she asks?
And he lies wounded.—By her side the Schoolboy!

(*Breaking out.*)

A scandal! What? This splendid marriage broken off!
All the jealous fools of the quarter and the streets around,
How they will laugh! The surgeon quick! What if 't
were fatal?

(*To Sophia, in utmost fury.*)

You marry him!

(*To Octavian, subduing his rudeness, out of respect to Rofrano's
rank to obsequious civility.*)

And may I now, in all humility, request
Your Lordship to retire as speedily from hence as may be
And ne'er again these doors to darken!

(*To Sophia.*)

Mark my words—
You marry him, and if he now should bleed to death,
His lifeless corpse will be your bridegroom!

(*The Doctor indicates by a reassuring gesture that the wounded man
is in no danger. Octavian looks for his hat, which had fallen
under the feet of the servants. A maid hands it to him with a
curtsey. Faninal makes an obeisance of exaggerated civility, but
unmistakable significance to Octavian. Octavian realizes that he
must go, but is longing to speak one more word to Sophia. He
replies to Faninal's obeisance by an equally ceremonious bow.
Sophia hastens to speak the following words ere Octavian is out
of earshot. With a curtsey.*)

SOPHIA: That man I will not marry living, and not dead
First will I lock me in my chamber and starve!

FANINAL (*furious, after he has again made an angry bow to Octavian, to
which he promptly responds*):

Ah! Lock yourself in—I've men enough to drag you
To a coach if I command them.

SOPHIA (*curtseying again*):

Then on the way to church from out the coach I jump!

85

FANINAL (*mit dem gleichen Spiel zwischen ihr und Octavian, der immer einen Schritt gegen den Ausgang tut, aber von Sophie in diesem Augenblick nicht los kann*):
Ah! Springst noch aus dem Wagen! Na, ich sitz' neben dir,
werd' dich schon halten!

SOPHIE (*mit einem neuen Knicks*):
Geb' halt dem Pfarrer am Altar
Nein anstatt Ja zur Antwort!

(*Der Haushofmeister indessen macht die Leute abtreten. Die Bühne leert sich. Nur die Lerchenauschen Leute bleiben bei ihrem Herrn zurück.*)

FANINAL (*mit gleichem Spiel*):
Ah! Gibst Nein statt Ja zur Antwort.
Ich steck' dich in ein Kloster stante pede!
Marsch! Mir aus meinen Augen! Lieber heut als morgen!
Auf Lebenszeit!

SOPHIE (*erschrocken*):
Ich bitt' Sie um Pardon! Bin doch kein schlechtes Kind!
Vergeben Sie mir nur dies eine Mal!

FANINAL (*hält sich in Wut die Ohren zu*):
Auf Lebenszeit! Auf Lebenszeit!

OCTAVIAN (*schnell, halblaut*):
Sei Sie nur ruhig, Liebste, um alles!
Sie hört von mir!
(*Duenna stösst Octavian, sich zu entfernen.*)

FANINAL: Auf Lebenzeit!

DUENNA (*zieht Sophie mit sich nach links*):
So geh' doch nur dem Vater aus den Augen!

(*Zieht sie zur Türe links hinaus, schliesst die Tür. Octavian ist zur Mitteltür abgegangen. Baron, umgeben von seiner Dienerschaft, Duenna, zwei Mägden, den Italienern und dem Arzt, wird auf einem aus Sitzmöbeln improvisierten Ruhebett jetzt in ganzer Gestalt sichtbar.*)

FANINAL (*schreit nochmals durch die Türe links, durch die Sophie abgegengen ist*):
Auf Lebenszeit!
(*Eilt dann dem Baron entgegen.*)
Bin überglücklich! Muss Eu'r Liebden embrassieren!

BARON (*dem bei der Umarmung der Arm wehgetan*):
Oh! Oh! Jesus Maria!

FANINAL (*nach rechts hin in neuer Wut*):
Luderei! Ins Kloster!
(*Nach der Mitteltür.*)
Ein Gefängnis!
Auf Lebenszeit!

BARON: Is gut! Is gut! Ein Schluck von was zu trinken!

FANINAL: Ein Wein? Ein Bier? Ein Hippokras mit Ingwer?

DER ARZT (*macht eine ängstlich abwehrende Bewegung*).

FANINAL: (*with similar by-play between himself and Octavian, who each time takes a step towards the door, but cannot tear himself from Sophia at such a moment*):

> From the coach you'll jump, Miss! Well, I'll be by your side,
>
> And I'll know how to hold you.

SOPHIA (*courtseys again*):

> Then at the altar I shall say,
> "No," and not "Yes."—No, never!

(*The Major-Domo has in the meantime made the servants leave. The stage is gradually cleared. Only Lerchenau's servants remain with their master.*)

FANINAL (*with similar by-play*):

> Ah! Say No and never Yes at the altar!
> I send you to a convent on the instant!
> March! Out of my sight! Hussy! Better now than to-morrow.
>
> For all your life!

SOPHIA (*alarmed*):

> Pray pardon, I implore! I am your loving child—
> Forgive me, father, but this once, this once.

FANINAL (*furious, closing his ears*):

> For all your life! For all your life!

OCTAVIAN (*whispers*):

> Speak not thus rashly, dearest, for my sake!
> You'll hear from me.
>
> (*The Duenna pushes Octavian towards the door.*)

FANINAL: For all your life!

> (*The Duenna takes Sophia with her to the left.*)

DUENNA: Go, get you gone from out your father's sight now.

(*Takes her out by the door to the left—closes the door. Octavian goes out by the centre door. The Baron, surrounded by his servants, the Duenna, two Maids, the Italians and the Doctor, is now discovered lying on a couch improvized out of several chairs.*)

FANINAL (*shouts once more through the door after Sophia*):

> For all your life!
>
> (*Hurries towards the Baron.*)
>
> What joy unbounded! I must embrace you, my dear Baron!

BARON (*whose arm has been hurt by the embrace*):

> Oh! Oh! Jesus Maria!

FANINAL (*turning to the right, his anger rising again*):

> Hussy you! A convent!
>
> (*Turning to the centre.*)
>
> A prison cell!
> For all your life!

BARON: Let be! Let be! Some drink, for I am thirsty.

FANINAL: Some wine? some beer? Some hippicras with ginger?

> (**The Doctor makes a nervous deprecating gesture.**)

FANINAL (*jammernd*):

So einen Herrn zurichten miserabel!
In meinem Stadtpalais! Sie heirat' ihn um desto früher!
Bin Manns genug!

BARON (*matt*):

Is gut, is gut!

FANINAL (*nach der Tür links, in aufflammender Wut*):

Bin Manns genug!

(*Zum Baron.*)

Küss Ihm die Hand für Seine Güt und Nachsicht.
Gehört alles Ihm im Haus. Ich lauf'—ich bring' Ihm—

(*Nach links.*)

Ein Kloster ist zu gut!

(*Zum Baron.*)

Sei'n ausser Sorg'.

(*Sehr devot.*)

Weiss, was ich Satisfaktion Ihm schuldig bin.

(*Stürzt ab. Desgleichen gehen Duenna und Mägde ab. Die beiden Italiener sind schon während des Obigen fortgeschlichen.*)

BARON (*halb aufgerichtet*):

Da lieg' ich! Was ei'm Kavalier nit all's passieren kann
in dieser Wienerstadt!
Wär nicht mein Gusto hier,—da ist eins gar zu sehr in
Gottes Hand,
wär lieber schon daheim!

(*Ein Diener ist aufgetreten, eine Kanne Weines zu servieren.*)

BARON (*will trinken, da macht er eine Bewegung, die ihm Schmerzen verursacht*):

Oh! Oh! Der Satan! Oh! Oh! Sakramentsverfluchter
Bub',
nit trocken hinterm Ohr und fuchtelt mit 'n Spadi!

(*In immer grösserer Wut.*)

Wällischer Hundsbub' das! Dich sollt' ich nur erwischen
In Hundezwinger sperr' ich dich, bei meiner Seel',
in Hühnerstall! In Schweinekofen!
Tät' dich kuranzen! Solltest alle Engel singen hör'n!

(*Zu dem Faninalschen Diener.*)

Schenk' Er nur ein da, schnell!

DIE LERCHENAUISCHEN (*gedämpft*):

Wenn ich dich erwisch',
Du liegst unter'm Tisch.
Wart', dich hau' i z'samm,
dass dich Gott verdamm'!

BARON (*zum Arzt gewandt*):

Herr Medicus, verfüg' Er sich voraus!
Mach' Er das Bett aus lauter Federbetten.
Ich komm'. Erst aber trink' ich noch. Marschier' Er nur
indessen.

FANINAL (*plaintively*) : So nobly born, so nobly born, so mauled and so
                                                                    insulted!
                      And in my Palace too! You'll marry him but all the
                                                                    sooner.
                      I'm master here!

BARON (*wearily*) :
                      Let be! Let be!

FANINAL (*towards the door on the left, his anger rising*) :
                      I'm master here!
                                                        (*To the Baron.*)
                      I kiss your hand. My thanks for such indulgence.
                      Command all that is in this house! I run—I bring you . . .
                                                        (*To the left.*)
                      A convent is too good.
                                                        (*To the Baron.*)
                      Pray have no fear.
                                                        (*Very obsequious.*)
                      I know what satisfaction, is your due from me.
(*Faninal rushes off. The Duenna and the Maids follow. The two
Italians had already slunk off during the preceding scene.*)

BARON (*half sitting up*) :
                      Here am I! Now! What curious adventures may befall a
                                                                    man
                      In this Metropolis.
                      Not all are to my taste—Here is one far too much the
                                                                    sport of fate!
                      'Tis better at home.
(*A Footman enters and serves wine. The Baron tries to drink and
makes a movement which causes him pain.*)

BARON :   Oh! Oh! The Devil! Oh! Oh! Oh, a plague upon that
                                                                    boy!
                      A baby, scarcely breeched, and plays with swords already.
                                                        (*With growing passion.*)
                      Curséd Italian hound! Wait till I catch your Lordship!
                      In my kennel, I'll teach you to fight, upon on my soul!
                      With cocks and hens I'll house you.
                      Egad, I'll trounce you! Make you hear the angels sing!
                                                        (*To Faninal's Footman.*)
                      Give me some wine there, quick!

LERCHENAU'S SERVANTS (*with hollow voices*) :
                      We will towzle you!
                      Beat you black and blue!
                      We will do for you,
                      Beat you black and blue!

BARON (*to the Doctor*) :
                      And now, my friend, precede me to my room,
                      And make my bed, and let it be all feathers.
                      I come, but first, another draught
                      Remember what I told you.

89

(Der Arzt geht ab mit dem Leiblakai. Annina ist durch den Vorsaal hereingekommen und schleicht sich verstohlen heran, einen Brief in der Hand).

BARON *(vor sich leise, den zweiten Becher leerend)*:

Ein Federbett. Zwei Stunden noch zu Tisch. Werd' Zeitlang haben.

„Ohne mich, ohne mich, jeder Tag dir so bang,
mit mir, mit mir, keine Nacht dir zu lang."

(Annina stellt sich so, dass der Baron sie sehen muss und winkt ihm geheimnisvoll mit dem Brief.)

BARON: Für mich?

ANNINA *(näher)*:

Von der Bewussten.

BARON: Wer soll da gemeint sein?

ANNINA *(ganz nahe)*:

Nur eigenhändig, insgeheim zu übergeben.

BARON: Luft da!

(Die Diener treten zurück, nehmen den Faninalschen ohne weiteres die Weinkanne ab und trinken sie leer.)

BARON: Zeig' Sie den Wisch!

(Reisst mit der Linken den Brief auf. Versucht ihn zu lesen, indem er ihn sehr weit von sich weghält.)

Such' Sie in meiner Taschen meine Brillen.

(Misstrauisch, da sie sich dazu anschickt.)

Nein! Such' Sie nicht! Kann Sie Geschriebnes lesen? Da.

ANNINA *(nimmt und liest)*:

„Herr Kavalier! Den morgigen Abend hätt' i frei.
Sie ham mir schon g'fall'n, nur g'schamt
hab' i mi von der fürstli'n Gnad'n,
weil i noch gar so jung bin. Das bewusste Mariandel,
Kammerzofel und Verliebte.
Wenn der Herr Kavalier den Nam' nit schon vergessen hat.
I wart' auf Antwort."

BARON *(entzückt)*:

Sie wart' auf Antwort.
Geht all's recht am Schnürl so wie z' Haus
und hat noch einen andern Schick dazu.
Ich hab' halt schon einmal ein lerchenauisch Glück.
Komm' Sie nach Tisch, geb' Ihr die Antwort nachher schriftlich.

ANNINA: Ganz zu Befehl, Herr Kavalier. Vergessen nich der Botin?

BARON *(sie überhörend, vor sich)*:

„Ohne mich, ohne mich jeder Tag dir so bang."

ANNINA *(dringlicher)*:

Vergessen nicht der Botin, Euer Gnad'n?

90

(The Doctor goes out with the Body Servant. Annina has entered through the ante-room and comes up to him mysteriously with a letter in her hand.)

BARON *(to himself softly, emptying the second cup)* :

A feather bed! Two hours yet till I dine, and no distra ·
tion.

"Without me, without me, slowly pass all the days,
With me, with me, time will seem short always.'

(Annina places herself so that the Baron must see her and makes mysterious signs to him with her letter.)

For me?

ANNINA *(nearer)* :

From her you know of!

BARON : And whom may you mean, pray!

ANNINA *(coming quite close)* :

Into your own 'ands I must give it, and in secret.

BARON : Room there!

(His servants retire without more ado, take the wine-can from Faninal's servant and empty it.)

Show me the thing!

(Tears the letter open with his left hand. Tries to read it, holding it as far as possible from him.)

Look in my pocket for my glasses.

(Suspiciously, as she is searching.)

No! Do not look. Are you a scholar? Read it
There—

ANNINA *(takes the letter and reads)* :

"Wors'ipful Sir! To-morrow at nightfall I am free!
You pleased me, but I felt it shame,
Ven 'er 'ighness was looking, to say it,
For I am still a young thing,
She you know of, Mariandel,
Tirewoman, and your sweetheart,
And I hope that your Lords'ip's 'onour 'as not forgotten
me.

I wait an answer."

BARON *(delighted)* :

She waits an answer!
It all goes on wheels—as at home,
And, look you, what an air of fashion it has.

(Very merry.)

I have all the luck of the Lerchenaus—
Come when I've dined—I'll give the answer then in
writing.

ANNINA : Your most obedient servant, my Lord.
Your Lords'ip v'on't forget me?

BARON *(not noticing her—to himself)* :

"Without me, without me, slowly pass all the days."

ANNINA *(importunately)* :

Your Lords'ip 'as forgotten ze bearer

BARON: Schon gut.

"Mit mir, mit mir keine Nacht dir zu lang."

ANNINA (*macht nochmals eine Gebärde des Geldforderns*).

BARON: Das später. Alls auf einmal. Dann zum Schluss.
Sie wart' auf Antwort! Tret' Sie ab indessen.
Schaff' Sie ein Schreibzeug in mein Zimmer, bin dort
drüben,
dass ich die Antwort dann diktier'.

ANNINA (*geht ab, nicht ohne mit einer drohenden Gebärde hinter des
Barons Rücken angezeigt zu haben, dass sie sich bald für seinen
Geiz rächen werde*).

BARON (*tut noch einen letzten Schluck, er geht, von seinen Leuten begleitet, seinem Zimmer zu*):
"Mit mir, mit mir keine Nacht dir zu lang!"

BARON: Enough—
              "With me, with me, time will seem short always—
                            (*Annina makes another begging gesture.*)
              Afterward—all together—at the end.
              "I wait an answer." In the meantime leave me,
              Bring to my room soon all that you need for writing,
              And I'll dictate you my reply.

(Annina goes out, not without indicating by a threatening gesture be-
hind the Baron's back, that she will be even with him for his nig-
gardliness. The Baron takes a last sip of wine, and goes toward
his room, accompanied by his people.)

BARON: "With me, with me, time shall seem short always!"
                            END OF ACT TWO.

DRITTER AUFZUG

Ein Extrazimmer in einem Gasthaus. Im Hintergrunde links ein Alkoven, darin ein Bett. Der Alkoven durch einen Vorhang verschliessbar, der sich auf- und zuziehn lässt. Vorne rechts Türe ins Nebenzimmer. Rechts steht ein für zwei Personen gedeckter Tisch, auf diesem ein grosser vielarmiger Leuchter. In der Mitte rückwärts Türe auf den Korridor. Daneben links ein Büffet. Rechts rückwärts ein blindes Fenster, vorne links ein Fenster auf die Gasse. Armleuchter mit Kerzen auf den Seitentischen, sowie an den Wänden. Es brennt nur je eine Kerze in den Leuchtern und auf den Seitentischen. Das Zimmer halbdunkel.

Annina steht da, als Dame in Trauer gekleidet. Valzacchi richtet ihr den Schleier, zupft da und dort das Kleid zurecht, tritt zurück, mustert sie, zieht einen Crayon aus der Tasche, untermalt ihr die Augen. Die Türe rechts wird vorsichtig geöffnet, ein Kopf erscheint, verschwindet wieder, dann kommt eine nicht ganz unbedenklich aussehende, aber ehrbar gekleidete Alte hereingeschlüpft, öffnet lautlos die Tür und lässt respektvoll Octavian eintreten, in Frauenkleidern, mit einem Häubchen, wie es die Bürgermädchen tragen.

Octavian, hinter ihm die Alte, gehen auf die beiden anderen zu, werden sogleich von Valzacchi bemerkt, der in seiner Arbeit innehält und sich vor Octavian verneigt. Annina erkennt nicht sofort den Verkleideten, sie kann sich vor Staunen nich fassen, knickst dann tief. Octavian greift in die Tasche (nich wie eine Dame, sondern wie ein Herr und man sieht, dass er unter dem Reifrock Männerkleider und Reitstiefel anhat, aber ohne Sporen) und wirft Valzacchi eine Börse zu.

Valzacchi und Annina küssen ihm die Hände, Annina richtet noch an Octavians Brusttuch. Indessen sind fünf verdächtige Herren unter Vorsichtsmassregeln eingetreten. Valzacchi bedeutet sie mit einem Wink zu warten. Sie stehen nahe der Türe. Eine Uhr schlägt halb. Valzacchi zieht seine Uhr, zeigt Octavian: es ist hohe Zeit. Octavian geht eilig ab, gefolgt von der Alten, die als seine Begleiterin fungiert. Annina geht zum Spiegel (alles mit Vorsicht, jedes Geräusch vermeidend) arrangiert sich noch, zieht dann einen Zettel hervor, woraus sie ihre Rolle zu lernen scheint. Valzacchi nimmt indessen die Verdächtigen nach vorne, indem er mit jeder Gebärde die Notwendigkeit höchster Vorsicht andeutet. Die Verdächtigen folgen ihm auf den Zehen nach der Mitte. Er bedeutet ihrer einem, ihm zu folgen: lautlos, ganz lautlos. Führt ihn an die Wand rechts, öffnet lautlos eine Falltür unfern des gedeckten Tisches, lässt den Mann hinabsteigen, schliesst wieder die Falltür. Dann winkt er zwei zu sich, schleicht ihnen voran bis an die Eingangstüre, steckt den Kopf heraus, vergewissert sich, dass niemand zusieht, winkt die zwei zu sich, lässt sie dort hinaus. Dann schliesst er die Türe, führt die beiden letzten leise an die Türe zum Nebenzimmer voran, schiebt sie hinaus. Winkt Annina zu sich, geht mit ihr leise links ab, die Türe lautlos hinter sich schliessend. Er kommt wieder herein, klatscht in die Hände. Der eine Versteckte hebt sich mit halben Leib aus dem Boden hervor. Zugleich erscheinen

ACT THREE

A private room in an inn. At the back to the left a recess (in it a bed.) The recess is separated from the room by a curtain, which can be drawn.

At the centre, towards the left, a fire-place with a fire, over it a mirror. In front on the left, a door leading to a side room. Opposite the fire-place is a table laid for two, on which stands a large, many-branched candlestick. At the back, in the centre, a door leading to the corridor. Next to it, on the right, a sideboard.

At the back, on the right, a blind window; in front, on the right, a window looking on the street. Candelabra with candles on the sideboard and on the chimney piece, and sconces on the walls.

Only one candle is burning in each candlestick on the chimneypiece. The room is in semi-darkness.

Annina discovered, dressed as a lady in mourning. Valzacchi is arranging her veil, putting her dress to right, takes a step backwards, surveys her, takes a crayon from his pocket and paints her eyes.

The door on the left is opened cautiously, a head appears, and vanishes. Then a not unsuspicious-looking but decently dressed old woman slips in, opens the door silently and respectfully introduces Octavian, in female clothes, with a cap such as girls of the middle classes wear. Octavian, followed by the old woman, moves towards the others. Valzacchi is at once aware of them, stops in his occupation, and bows to Octavian. Annina does not at once recognize him in his disguise. She cannot restrain her astonishment, and curtseys low. Octavian feels in his pocket (not like a woman, but like a man, and one sees that under his skirt he is wearing riding boots without spurs) and throws a purse to Valzacchi; Valzacchi and Annina kiss his hands Annina puts a finishing touch to his kerchief.

Five suspicious looking men enter very cautiously from the left. Valzacchi makes them a sign to wait. They stand at the left, near the door.

A clock strikes the half-hour. Valzacchi takes out his watch; shows it to Octavian; it is high time. Octavian hurries out to the left, followed by the old woman, who acts as his duenna. Valzacchi leads the suspicious looking men to the front, impressing on them with every gesture the necessity of extreme caution. Annina goes to the mirror (all the while cautiously avoiding every noise) completes her disguise; then draws from a pocket a piece of paper, from which she seems to be learning a part. The suspicious looking men follow Valzacchi on tiptoe to the centre. He signs to one of them to follow him noiselessly, quite noiselessly, leads him to the wall on the right, noiselessly opens a trapdoor not far from the table, makes the man descend, closes the trapdoor; then he summons the others to his side, slinks in front of them to the door of the room, puts his head out, assures himself that they are not observed, makes a sign to the two to come to him, and lets them out. Then he closes the door, directs the two remaining men to precede him to the door which leads to the side room, pushes them out, signs to Annina to come to him, goes out with her silently to the left, and noiselessly closes the door behind him. He returns—claps his hands.

über dem Bett und andern Stellen Köpfe. Auf Valzacchis Wink verschwinden dieselben ebenso plötzlich, die geheimen Schiebtüren schliessen sich ohne Geräusch. Valzacchi sieht abermals nach der Uhr, geht nach rückwärts, öffnet die Eingangstür, dann zieht er ein Feuerzeug hervor und beginnt eifrig die Kerzen auf dem Tisch anzuzünden. Ein Kellner und ein Kellnerjunge kommen gelaufen mit zwei Stöcken zum Kerzenanzünden. Entzünden die Leuchter auf dem Kamin, auf dem Büfett, dann die zahlreichen Wandarme. Sie haben die Tür hinter sich offen gelassen, man hört aus dem Vorsaal (im Hintergrunde) Tanzmusik spielen. Valzacchi eilt zur Mitteltür, öffnet dienstbeflissen auch den zweiten Flügel, springt unter Verneigung zur Seite.

Baron Ochs erscheint, den Arm in der Schlinge. Octavian an der Linken führend, hinter ihm der Leiblakai. Baron mustert den Raum. Octavian sieht herum, läuft an den Spiegel, richtet sein Haar. Baron bemerkt den Kellner und Kellnerjungen, die noch mehr Kerzen anzünden wollen, winkt ihnen, sie sollten es sein lassen. In ihrem Eifer bemerken sie es nicht.

BARON (*ungeduldig, reisst den Kellnerjungen vom Stuhl, auf den er gestigen war, löscht einige ihm zunächst brennende Kerzen mit der Hand aus. Valzacchi zeigt dem Baron diskret den Alkoven und durch eine Spalte des Vorhanges das Bett. Der Wirt mit mehrerer Kellnern eilt herbei, den vornehmen Gast zu begrüssen*).

WIRT: Haben Euer Gnaden noch weitere Befehle?

KELLNER: Befehl'n mehr Lichter?

WIRT: Ein grösseres Zimmer?

KELLNER: Befehlen mehr Silber auf den Tisch?

BARON (*eifrig beschäftig mit einer Serviette, die er vom Tisch genommen und entfaltet hat, alle ihm erreichbaren Kerzen auszulöschen*):
             Verschwindt's! Macht mir das Madel net verruckt
             Was will die Musik? Hab' sie nicht bestellt.
                        (*Löscht weitere Kerzen aus.*)

WIRT: Schaffen vielleicht, dass man sie näher hört
             Im Vorsaal da als Tafelmusik.

BARON: Lass Er die Musik, wo sie ist.
    (*Bemerkt das Fenster rechts rückwärts im Rücken des gedeckten Tisches.*)
             Was ist da für ein Fenster da?
                        (*Probiert, ob es hereinzieht.*)

WIRT: Ein blindes Fenster nur.
                        (*Verneigt sich.*)

             Darf aufgetragen werd'n?
                        (*Alle fünf Kellner wollen abeilen.*)

BARON: Halt, was woll'n die Maikäfer da?
KELLNER (*an der Tür*):
             Servier'n, Euer Gnaden.

BARON (*winkt ab*):
             Brauch' niemand nicht.
                        (*Als sie nicht gehen, heftig.*)

             Packt's Euch! Servieren wird mein Kammerdiener da.
             Einschenken tu' ich selber. Versteht Er?

96

The man who is hidden rises to his waist from the trapdoor. **At the** *same moment heads appear above the bed and in other places. At a sign from Valzacchi they disappear as suddenly—the secret panels close without a sound. Valazacchi again looks at his watch, goes to the back, opens the door. Then he produces a tinder-box and busily lights the candles on the table.*

A Waiter and a Boy run in with tapers for lighting candles, and light the candles on the chimney, on the sideboard, and the numerous sconces. They have left the door open behind them, dance music is heard from the anteroom at the back.

Valzacchi hurries to the centre door, opens it respectfully (both wings) and bowing low springs aside.

Baron Ochs appears, his arm in a sling, leading Octavian by his left, followed by his Body Servant The Baron surveys the room. Octavian looks round, runs to the mirror and arranges his hair. The Baron notices the Waiter and the Boy, who are about to light more candles, and signs to them to stop. In their preoccupation they do not notice him. The Baron, in his impatience, pulls the Boy from the chair on to which he has climbed, and extinguishes some of the candles nearest him with his hand. Valzacchi discreetly points out the recess to him (and through an opening of the curtains the bed).

(Enter the Landlord.)

LANDLORD (*hurrying forward to greet the noble guest*):
   Has your Lordship any further wishes?

WAITERS: D'you lack more candles?

LANDLORD: A larger apartment?

WAITERS: More lights we'll bring your Lordship if you wish—
   More silver—

BARON (*busily engaged in extinguishing all the candles in his reach with a napkin which he has taken from the table and unfolded.*)
   Be off! Such talk will turn the hussy's brain.

(Extinguishes more candles.)

   What is that music? I commanded none.

LANDLORD: They can come near if 'tis your Lordship's wish—
   To play to you in yonder anteroom.

BARON: Best let them stay there, as they are.
   (*Notices the blind window to the right behind the table.*)
   Tell me, what means that window there?

(Tries it.)

LANDLORD: That window? That is blind.

(Bows.)

   Can supper now begin?

(All five waiters make as if to hurry off.)

BARON: Stop! What mean those grinning apes?

WAITERS: To wait upon your Lordship.

BARON (*makes a sign to them to go*):
   I need no help. Be off!
   My man there will serve all the meats to us.
   Myself I'll fill the glasses. Now leave us.

97

*(Valzacchi bedeutet sie, den Willen seiner Gnaden wortlos zu respek-
tieren. Schiebt alle zur Tür hinaus.)*

BARON *(löscht aufs neue eine Anzahl Kerzen aus, darunter mit einiger
Mühe die hoch an der Wand brennenden, zu Valzacchi)*:

Er ist ein braver Kerl. Wenn er mir hilft, die Rechnung
'runterdrucken,
Dann fallt was ab für Ihn. Kost' sicher hier ein Marter-
geld.

(Valzacchi unter Verneigung ab. — Octavian ist nun fertig.)

BARON *(führt ihn zu Tisch, sie setzen sich)*.

*(Der Lakai am Büffet sieht mit unverschämter Neugierde der Ent-
wicklung des tete-a-tete entgegen, stellt Karaffen mit Wein vom
Büffet auf den Esstisch. Baron schenkt ein. Octavian nippt.
Baron küsst Octavian die Hand. Octavian entzieht ihm die Hand.
Baron winkt den Lakaien abzugehen, muss es mehrmals wieder-
holen, bis die Lakaien endlich gehen.)*

OCTAVIAN *(schiebt sein Glas zurück)*:

Nein, nein, nein, nein! I trink' kein Wein.

BARON: Geh, Herzel, was denn? Mach' doch keine Faxen.

OCTAVIAN: Nein, nein, i bleib' net da.

(Springt auf, tut, als wenn er fort wollte.)

BARON *(packt sie mit seiner Linken)*:

Jetzt komm' Sie. Setz' Sie sich schön.
Kommt gleich wer mit'n Essen. Hat Sie denn kein' Hunger
nicht?

(Legt ihr die Hand um die Taille.)

OCTAVIAN *(wirft dem Baron schmachtende Blicke zu)*:

O weh, wo Sie doch ein Bräutigam tun sein.

(Wehrt ihn ab.)

BARON: Ach, lass Sie schon einmal das fade Wort!

Sie hat doch einen Kavalier vor sich
und keinen Seifensieder:
Ein Kavalier lässt alles,
was ihn nicht konveniert,
da draussen vor der Tür. Hier sitzt kein Bräutigam
und keine Kammerjungfer nicht:
Hier sitzt mit seiner Allerschönsten ein Verliebter beim
Souper.

(Zieht sie an sich.)

OCTAVIAN *(lehnt sich kokett in den Sessel zurück, mit halbgeschlossenen
Augen)*.

BARON *(erhebt sich, der Moment für den ersten Kuss scheint ihm gekommen. Wie sein Gesicht dem der Partnerin ganz nahe ist,
durchzuckt ihn jäh die Aehnlichkeit mit Octavian. Er fährt
zurück und greift unwillkürlich nach dem verwundeten Arm)*:

Ist ein Gesicht! Verfluchter Bub'!
Verfolgt mich alser wacher und im Traum!

OCTAVIAN *(öffnet die Augen und blickt ihn frech und kokett an)*:
Was meint Er denn?

(Valzacchi signing to them to respect his Lordship's wishes without demur, pushes them all out of the door. The Baron continues to extinguish the candles, among them some high on the walls which he reaches with difficulty.)

BARON: You are an honest fellow. If you can help me reduce the reckoning,
There will be vails for you. 'Tis surely very costly here.
(Exit Valzacchi, bowing.)

(Octavian has now finished arranging his hair. The Baron leads him to the table. The Body Servant at the sideboard contem-plates the developments of the tête-à-tête with impudent curi- osity. He places bottles of wine from the sideboard on the table. The Baron pours out wine. Octavian takes a sip. The Baron kisses Octavian's hand. Octavian withdraws his hand. The Baron signs to the lackey to withdraw, but he has to repeat the signal several times before he goes.)

OCTAVIAN *(pushing back his glass)*:
What do you think? No wine I drink.

BARON: Come, sweetheart, why not? Now let's have no flim-flams.

OCTAVIAN: No, no, no, no, I will not stay.
(Jumps up as if he would go away.)

BARON *(seizing him with his left hand)*:
Sit down now, take your place, here.
They'll soon bring supper . . . Then we'll fall to with appetite.

(Puts his arm round his waist. Octavian casts languid glances at him.)

OCTAVIAN: Oh dear! Oh! to think you're promised and all!
(Keeping him off.)

BARON: Have done with such old wives' tales once for all.
You see here nothing but a gentleman,
None of your common fellows—
A gentleman forgets
And leaves behind him everything
That is not to his taste. Here sits no promised man,
Here at my side no waiting-maid—
Here sit we two and sup, a lover and his lass. That merely,—nothing more.

(Draws him to his side. Octavian leans back coquettishly in his chair, with half-closed eyes. The Baron rises. The moment for the first kiss seems to have come. As his face is close to that of his companion, the resemblance to Octavian strikes him like a blow. He starts back and half unconsciously feels his wounded arm.)

BARON: One face, I swear. Accurséd boy . . .
Pursues me when I'm waking and all night.

OCTAVIAN *(opening his eyes and looking at him with impudent coquetry)*:
Lawk! How you talk!

99

BARON: Sieht einem ähnlich, einem gottverfluchten Kerl!

OCTAVIAN: Ah geh'! Das hab' i no net g'hört!

BARON (*nun wieder versichert, dass es die Zofe ist, zwingt sich zu einem Lächeln. Aber der Schreck ist ihm nicht ganz aus den Gliedern. Er muss Luft schöpfen und aer Kuss bleibt aufgeschoben. Der Mann unter der Falltür öffnet zu früh und kommt zum Vorschein*).

OCTAVIAN (*der ihm gegenübersitzt, winkt ihm eifrig zu verschwinden. Der Mann verschwindet sofort. Baron, der, um den unangenehmen Eindruck von sich abzuschütteln, ein paar Schritte getan hat und sie von rückwärts umschlingen und küssen will, sieht gerade noch den Mann. Er erschrickt heftig, zeigt hin*).

OCTAVIAN (*als verstände er nicht*):
Was ist mit Ihm?

BARON (*auf die Stelle deutend, wo die Erscheinung verschwunden ist*):
Was war den das? Hat Sie den nicht gesehn?

OCTAVIAN: Da is ja nix.

BARON: Da is nix?
(*Nun wieder ihr Gesicht angstvoll musternd.*)
So?
Und da ist auch nix?
(*Fährt mit der Hand über ihr Gesicht.*)

OCTAVIAN: Da is mei' G'sicht.

BARON (*atmet schwer, schenkt sich ein Glas Wein ein*):
Da is Ihr G'sicht — und da is nix — mir scheint,
ich hab' die Kongestion.
(*Setzt sich schwer, es ist ihm ängstlich zumute. Die Tür geht auf, man hört draussen wieder die Musik. Der Lakai kommt und serviert.*)

OCTAVIAN (*sehr weich*):
Die schöne Musik!

BARON (*wieder sehr laut*):
Is mei Leiblied, weiss Sie das?

OCTAVIAN (*horcht auf die Musik*):
Da muss ma weinen.

BARON: Was?

OCTAVIAN: Weil's gar so schön is.

BARON: Was, weinen? Wär nicht schlecht.
Kreuzlustig muss Sie sein, die Musik geht ins Blut.
(*Sentimental.*)
G'spürt Sie's jetzt —
(*Winkt dem Lakaien abzugehen.*)
Auf die letzt, g'spürt Sie's dahier,
Dass Sie aus mir
Kann machen alles frei, was Sie nur will.

DER LAKAI (*geht zögernd ab, öffnet nochmals die Tür, schaut mit frecher Neugierde herein und verschwindet erst auf einen neuen heftigen Wink des Barons gänzlich*).

BARON :   You're like to some one—an accurséd scurvy boy—

OCTAVIAN :   Have done! Who can it be I'm like?

(The Baron has once again assured himself that it is the waiting-maid, and forces a smile. But he is not quite rid of his fright. He must take breath, and the kiss is postponed. The man under the trapdoor opens it too soon and appears. Octavian who is sitting opposite to him makes violent signs to him to get out of sight. He vanishes at once. The Baron, who to shake off the unpleasant impression, has taken a few steps and is on the point of embracing Octavian from behind, just catches a last glimpse of him. He is violently alarmed and points to the spot.)

OCTAVIAN *(does as if he did not understand.)*
          What's wrong with you?

BARON :   Gad! What was that?
          (Points to the spot where the apparition has vanished.)
          Did you see that man there?

OCTAVIAN :   There's nothing there.

BARON :   Nothing there?
                    (Again anxiously scanning Octavian's face.)
          No?
                         (Passing his hand over his face.)
          Nothing there, neither?

OCTAVIAN :   That is my face.

BARON *(breathing heavily, pours out a glass of wine)* :
          There is your face, and nothing there. It seems I have
                              a feverish brain—
(The door opens. The music from outside is heard again. The Body Servant comes and serves.)

OCTAVIAN *(very sweetly)* :
          The pretty music!

BARON :   'Tis the song that I like best.

OCTAVIAN :   It sets me weeping—

BARON :   What?

OCTAVIAN :   It is that pretty—

BARON :   What? Weeping? Why, what next?
          'Tis merry you should be. The music fires the blood.
                              (Sentimentally.)
          Do you still doubt, my dear?
                         (Signs to the Lackey to go.)
          Do you not see how 'tis with me?
          You now can make of me
          Your willing slave.

(The Lackey goes reluctantly—then opens the door again, and looks in with insolent curiosity and does not go till the Baron has made an angry sign.)

OCTAVIAN (*zurückgelehnt, wie zu sich selbt sprechend, mit unmässiger Traurigkeit*):
Es is ja eh als eins, es is ja eh als eins,
Was ein Herz noch so gach begehrt.
(*Indes der Baron ihre Hand fasst.*)
Geh', es is ja all's net drumi wert.

BARON (*lässt ihre Hand fahren*):
Ei, was denn? Is sehr wohl der Müh wert.

OCTAVIAN (*immer gleich melancholisch, wirft dem Baron schmachtende Blicke zu*):
Wie die Stund hingeht, wie der Wind verweht,
So sind wir bald alle zwei dahin.
Menschen sin' ma halt.
(*Schmachtender Blick auf den Baron.*)
Richtn's nichts mit G'walt,
Weint uns niemand nach, net dir net und net mir.

BARON: Macht Sie der Wein leicht immer so? Is ganz gewiss Ihr
Mieder,
das aufs Herzerl Ihr druckt.

OCTAVIAN (*mit geschlossenen Augen, gibt keine Antwort*).

BARON (*steht auf und will ihr das Mieder aufschnüren*):
Jetzt wird's frei mir a bisserl heiss.

(*Schnell entschlossen nimmt er seine Perücke ab und sucht sich einen Platz, sie abzulegen. Indem erblickt er ein Gesicht, das sich wieder im Alkoven zeigt und ihn anstarrt. Das Gesicht verschwindet gleich wieder. Er sagt sich: Kongestionen! und verscheucht den Schrecken, muss sich aber doch die Stirne abwischen. Sieht nun wieder die Zofe willenlos wie mit gelösten Gliedern dasitzen. Das ist stärker als alles, und er nähert sich ihr zärtlich. Da meint er wieder das Gesicht Octavians ganz nahe dem seinigen zu erkennen, und er fährt abermals zurück. Mariandl rührt sich kaum. Abermals verscheucht der Baron sich den Schreck, zwingt Munterkeit in sein Gesicht zurück, da fällt sein Auge abermals auf einen fremden Kopf, welcher aus der Wand hervorstarrt. Nun ist er masslos geängstigt, er schreit dumpf auf, ergreift die Tischglocke und schwingt sie wie rasend*):
Da und da und da und da!

(*Plötzlich springt das angeblich blinde Fenster auf. Annina in schwarzer Trauerkleidung erscheint und zeigt mit ausgestreckten Armen auf den Baron*).

BARON (*ausser sich vor Angst*):
Da und da und da und da!
(*Sucht sich den Rücken zu decken.*)

ANNINA: Er ist es! Es ist mein Mann! Er ist's!
(*Verschwindet.*)

BARON (*angstvoll*):
Was ist denn das?

OCTAVIAN: Das Zimmer ist verhext.
(*Schlägt ein Kreuz.*)

OCTAVIAN : 'Tis all one—'tis all one—
All our joys, and all our bitter pain,
In the end are they not all in vain?

(Leaning back in his chair as though to himself with exaggerated melancholy. The Baron takes his hand.)

BARON *(dropping his hand)* :
Why? What's this? No, sweetheart, not in vain.

(Octavian casts languishing glances at him.)

OCTAVIAN *(still very melancholy)* :
As the hours that go, as the winds that blow,
So we twain will pass away;
Flesh and blood are we, ruled by Fate's decree.

(With another languishing glance.)

When we die there's none to cry for us—not for you and
not for me.

BARON : Does wine make you so sad always?
'Tis surely your stomacher, that is pressing on your heart.

(Octavian with closed eyes does not answer. The Baron rises and tries to open his dress.)

It grows warm—I will take my ease.

(Without ado he takes off his wig, and seeks a place to deposit it. At this moment he espies a face which shows itself in the recess and glares at him. The face vanishes in a trice. He says to himself "Brainsick" and struggles with his fright, but has to mop his forehead. His eyes fall once again on the waiting-maid, sitting there helpless with relaxed limbs. That decides him, and he approaches tenderly. Then again he sees Octavian's face close to his own. He starts back again. "Mariandel" scarcely stirs. Once more the Baron fights with his terror, and forces himself to take a cheerful mien. Then his eyes alight again on a strange face, staring at him from the wall. Now he is beside himself with fright—he gives a muffled scream, seizes the handbell from the table and swings it distractedly.)

BARON : There! and there! and there! and there!

(Suddenly the presumed blind window is torn open. Annina in mourning appears and with outstretched arms points to the Baron.)

BARON *(beside himself with fear)* :
There! and there! and there! and there!

ANNINA : My husband! Yes, it is he! 'tis he! 'tis he!

(Vanishes.)

BARON : Zounds, what was that?

OCTAVIAN *(crosses himself)* :
The room is bewitched!

ANNINA (*gefolgt von dem Intriganten, der sie scheinbar anzuhalten sucht, vom Wirt und von drei Kellnern, stürzt zur Mitteltür herein; sie bedient sich des böhmisch-deutschen Akzents, aber gebildeter Sprechweise*):

Es ist mein Mann, ich leg' Beschlag auf ihn!
Gott ist mein Zerge, Sie sind meine Zeugen!
Gerichte! Hohe Obrigkeit! Die Kaiserin
muss ihn mir wiedergeben!

BARON (*zum Wirt*):

Was will das Weibsbild da von mir, Herr Wirt!
Was will der dort und der und der und der?

(*Zeigt nach allen Richtungen.*)

Der Teufel frequentier' sein gottverfluchtes Extrazimmer!

BARON (*hat sich eine kalte Kompresse auf den Kopf gelegt, hält sie mit der Linken fest, geht dann dicht auf die Kellner, den Wirt, zuletzt auf Annina zu, mustert sie ganz scharf, um sich über ihre Realität klar zu werden*):

ANNINA: Leupold bedenk':

Anton von Lerchenau, dort oben richtet dich ein Höherer!

(*Erschrickt zuerst heftig, dass sie in ihrer Anrede unterbrochen wird, fasst sich aber schnell.*)

BARON (*starrt sie fassungslos an*):

Kommt mir bekannt vor.

(*Sieht wieder auf Octavian.*)

Hab'n doppelte Gesichter alle miteinander.

WIRT: Die arme Frau Baronin!

KELLNER: Die arme Frau, die arme Frau Baronin!

VIER KINDER (*zwischen vier und zehn Jahren stürzen zu früh herein und auf den Baron zu*):

Papa! Papa! Papa!

ANNINA: Hörst du die Stimme deines Blutes!
Kinder, hebt eure Hände auf zu ihm!

BARON (*schlägt wütend mit einer Serviette, die er vom Tisch reisst, nach den Kindern; zum Wirt*):

Debarassier' Er mich von denen da.
Von der, von dem, von dem!

(*Zeigt nach allen Richtungen. Valzacchi indessen zu Octavian leise.*)

OCTAVIAN (*zu Valzacchi*):

Ist gleich wer fort, den Faninal zu holen?

VALZACCHI (*leise*):

Sogleich in Anfang. Wird sogleich zur Stelle sein.

WIRT (*im Rücken des Barons, leise*):

Halten zu Gnaden, gehen nit zu weit.
könnten recht böse Folgen g'spüren! Bitterböse!

BARON: Was? ich was g'spür'n? Von dem Möbel da?
Hab's nie nicht angerührt, nicht mit der Feuer zang'!

ANNINA (*schreit laut auf*):

Aah!

(Annina, followed by Valzacchi who makes pretence of holding her back, the Landlord, and three Waiters, rushes in at the centre door.)

ANNINA *(speaking with a Bohemian accent, but like a woman of education)*:

> I am his wife! I make a claim to him!
> Heav'n is my witness—you shall be my witness!
> The Law, the Ministers, Her Majesty
> Must restore him to my arms!

BARON *(to the Landlord)*:

> Landlord, what does this female want of me?
> What does he want? and he? and that one there?
>
> *(Pointing all round the room.)*
> Hell is let lose in this foul den of thieves.

(The Baron has put a cold compress on his head, holds it in its place with his left hand, then goes close up to the Landlord, the Waiters and Annina in turn, and scans them closely, as if to convince himself that they are real.)

ANNINA:

> Leopold, reflect!
> Anton of Lerchenau,
> Above us dwells a Judge that knoweth all!

LANDLORD AND WAITERS: Poor ill-used lady! Oh wretched, ill-used lady!

BARON *(stares in amazement at Annina)*:

> Surely I know you!
>
> *(Looks towards Octavian again.)*
> They all have double faces! All of them together!

(Four children between the ages of ten and four, entering too soon, rush towards the Baron.)

THE FOUR CHILDREN: Papa! Papa! Papa!

(Annina at first starts violently, so that her speech is interrupted, but soon regains her composure.)

ANNINA:

> Hear you the voices of your offspring?
> My children, raise your hands to him in pray'r!

(The Baron hits out at the children with a napkin which he takes from the table.)

BARON *(to the Landlord)*:

> Take all this crew away from here at once—
> Take her, take him, and him, and him!

OCTAVIAN: *(aside to Valzacchi)*:

> Have messengers been sent for Faninal?

VALZACCHI: Ere you 'ad come 'ere: in a moment you vill see 'im.

LANDLORD *(behind the Baron)*:

> Asking your pardon, venture not too far,
> Else might it end in harm for you—in harm most serious.

BARON:

> What? Harm to me from that old beldam there?
> Ne'er have I touched her—no, not with a pitchfork's end

ANNINA *(screams shrilly)*:

> Ah!

WIRT (*wie oben*):

Die Bigamie ist halt kein G'spass,
Is gar ein Kapitalverbrechen!

VALZACCHI (*zum Baron leise*):

Ik rat' Euer Gnaden, sei'n vorsiktig,
Die Sittenpolizei sein gar nicht tolerant!

BARON: Die Bigamie? Die Sittenpolizei?

(*Die Stimmen der Kinder nachahmend.*)
Papa, Papa, Papa?

(*Greift sich wie verloren an den Kopf, dann wütend.*)
Schmeiss' Er hinaus das Trauerpferd! Wer? Was? Er
will nicht?
Was? Polizei! Die Lackln woll'n nicht? Spielt das
Gelichter
Leicht alles unter einem Leder?
Sein wir in Frankreich? Sein wir unter Kurutzen?
Oder in kaiserlicher Hauptstadt?

(*Reisst das Gassenfenster auf.*)
Polizei!
Herauf da, Polizei: Gilt Ordnung herzustellen
Und einer Stand'sperson zu Hilf' zu eilen!

(*Man hört auf der Gasse laute Rufe nach der Polizei.*)

WIRT (*jammernd*):

Mein renommiertes Haus! Das muss mein Haus erleben.

DIE KINDER (*plärrend*):

Papa! Papa! Papa

(*Kommissarius mit zwei Wächtern treten auf. Alles rangiert sich,
ihnen Platz zu machen.*)

VALZACCHI (*zu Octavian*):

Oh weh, was maken wir?

OCTAVIAN: Verlass' Er sich auf mich und lass' Er's gehen, wie's geht.

VALZACCHI: Zu Euer Exzellenz Befehl!

KOMMISSARIUS (*scharf*):

Halt! Keiner rührt sich! Was ist los?
Wer hat um Hilf' geschrien? Wer hat Skandal gemacht?

BARON (*auf ihn zu, mit der Sicherheit des grossen Herrn*):

Is all's in Ordnung jetzt. Bin mit Ihm wohl zufrieden.
Hab' gleich verhofft, das in Wein all's so wie am Schnürl
geht.
(*Vergnügt.*)
Schaff' Er mir da das Pack vom Hals. Ich will in Ruh'
soupieren.

KOMMISSARIUS: Wer ist der Herr? Was gibt dem Herrn Befugnis?
Ist Er der Wirt?

(*Baron sperrt den Mund auf.*)

KOMMISSARIUS (*scharf*):

Dann halt' Er sich gefällig still
Und wart' Er, bis man ihn vernehmen wird.

LANDLORD: For bigamy is not a trifle,
It is a hanging matter—

VALZACCHI: I counsel zat your Lords'ip 'ave a care,
Ze police in zis town, it 'ave no mercy, Sir!

BARON: Bigamy! Pooh! A fig for your police!
(Mimicking the voices of the children.)
Papa! Papa! Papa!
(Striking his head as if in despair, then furiously.)
Turn out that whining Jezebel! Who? What? You will
not?
What? The Watch here! The rascals will not stir!
Is all this scurvy crew
Plotted to do me mischief?
Are we 'mong heathens? Or in France, or Turkey?
Or in this Empire's foremost city.
(Tears open the window that looks on to the street.)
The Watch!
The Watch, here! Hurry! Here! Quick, here, to quell
a riot!
Here is a man of quality in danger!
(Loud cries of "The Watch" are heard from the street.)

LANDLORD: Oh! my old inn disgraced! Oh, my fair reputation!

THE CHILDREN *(whinning)*:
Papa! Papa! Papa!
*(A Commissary of Police enters with two Constables. All stand back
to make way for them.)*

VALZACCHI: Alas! Vat can ve do?

OCTAVIAN: Put all your trust in me and happy chance.

VALZACCHI: Your 'umble servant to command.

COMMISSARY *(roughly)*:
Stop! No one stirs now! What's amiss?
Who was it called for help? Who was it broke the peace?

BARON *(going towards him with the self-confidence of a great gentleman)*:
The trouble now is passed. Right well done! I commend
you,
I knew at once that in Vienna there's no danger.
(Relieved.)
Drive me this crowd from out the room. I wish to sup
unhindered.

COMMISSARY: Who are you, pray? By what right do you meddle?
Is this your house?
(The Baron stands open-mouthed.)
Then hold your peace, withdraw,
And wait in patience till I need your evidence.

Baron (*retiriert sich etwas perplex, beginnt nach seiner Perücke zu suchen, die in dem Tumult abhanden gekommen ist und unauffindbar bleibt*).

Kommissarius (*setzt sich, die zwei Wächter nehmen hinter ihm Stellung*).

Kommissarius: Wo ist der Wirt?

Wirt (*devot*):
Mich dem Herrn Oberkommissarius schönstens zu rekom‑
mandieren.

Kommissarius: Die Wirtschaft da rekommandiert Ihn schlecht.
Bericht' Er jetzt! Von Anfang!

Wirt: Herr Kommissar! Der Herr Baron —

Kommissarius: Der grosse Dicke da? Wo hat er sein Paruckl?

Baron (*der die ganze Zeit gesucht hat*):
Das frag' ich Ihn!

Wirt: Das ist der Herr Baron von Lerchenau!

Kommissarius: Genügt nicht.

Baron: Was?

Kommissarius: Hat Er Personen nahebei,
Die für Ihn Zeugnis geben?

Baron: Gleich bei der Hand! Da hier mein Sekretär, ein Italiener.

Valzacchi (*wechselt mit Octavian einen Blick des Einverständnisses*):
Ik exkusier' mik. Ik weiss nix. Die Herr
kann sein Baron, kann sein auch nit. Ik weiss von nix.

Baron (*ausser sich*):
Das ist doch stark, wällisches Luder, falsches!
(*Geht mit erhobener Linken auf ihn los.*)

Kommissarius (*zum Baron, scharf*):
Fürs erste moderier' Er sich.

Octavian (*der bis jetzt ruhig rechts gestanden, tut nun, als ob er, in Verzweiflung hin und her irrend, den Ausweg nicht fände und das Fenster für eine Ausgangstür hielt*):
Oh mein Gott in die Erd'n möcht' ich sinken!
Heilige Mutter von Maria Taferl!

Kommissarius: Wer ist dort die junge Person?

Baron: Die? Niemand. Sie steht unter meiner Protektion!

Kommissarius: Er selber wird bald eine Protekion sehr nötig haben.
Wer ist das junge Ding, was macht Sie hier?
(*Blickt um sich.*)

Baron: Ist die Jungfer Faninal
Sophia Anna Barbara, eheliche Tochter
des wohlgeborenen Herrn von Faninal.
Wohnhaft am „Hof" im eignen Palais.

(The Baron retires in perplexity, begins to look for his wig, which had disappeared in the confusion and is not to be found. The Commissary seats himself. The two Constables take up their positior behind him.)

The Landlord first.

LANDLORD: By'r leave. Report myself. I'm landlord here, very much
at your service.

COMMISSARY: These goings-on do not speak well for you.
Now your report—The whole truth!

LANDLORD: It happened thus—His Lordship there . . .

COMMISSARY: That very fat man there? Where have you put your wig,
Sir?

BARON *(who has been searching all the time)*:
That I would from you.

LANDLORD: That is his Lordship, Baron Lerchenau—

COMMISSARY: First prove it.

BARON: What?

COMMISSARY: Is any person near at hand
Whom you can call as witness?

BARON: Yes, close at hand. There! My secretary, an Italian.

VALZACCHI *(exchanges glanches of intelligence with Octavian)*:
I can say nozzing! I not know. 'E may
Be Lerchenau—'e may be not. I do not know.

BARON *(beside himself)*:
That is too much. Lying Italian scum, you!
(Goes toward him with raised fist.)

COMMISSARY: 'Twere best you keep a civil tongue.
(Octavian, who up to now has stood quiet, now does as if, running about in despair, he could not find the way out, and mistook the window for the door.)

OCTAVIAN: Oh! I pray that the earth may start open
Under my feet and swallow me up!
(The Body rvant, who is much alarmed at the situation, suddenly has a l peful inspiration and hastily rushes out by the centre door.)

COMMISSARY: And that young woman there, who is she?

BARON: That? No one—she stands under my protection here—

COMMISSARY: Yourself will find protection needful soon.
Who is that girl, I say. Why is she here?
(Looks round.)

BARON: 'Tis young Mistress Faninal,
Sophia Anna Barbara, heiress and daughter
In lawful wedlock born to the most noble Lord
Faninal, domiciled here in the Hof.

(An der Tür haben sich Gasthofpersonal, andere Gäste, auch einige der Musiker aus dem andern Zimmer neugierig angesammelt. Herr von Faninal drängt sich durch sie durch, eilig aufgeregt in Hut und Mantel.)

FANINAL: Zur Stell'! Was wird von mir gewünscht?

                                 (Auf den Baron zu.)

Wie sieht Er aus?
War mir vermutend nicht zu dieser Stunde,
in ein gemeines Beisl depeschiert zu werden!

BARON *(sehr erstaunt und unangenehm berührt)*:

Wer hat Ihn hierher depeschiert? In des Dreiteufels
                                 Namen?

FANINAL *(halblaut zu ihm)*:

Was soll mir die saudumme Frag', Herr Schwiegersohn?
Wo Er mir schier die Tür einrennen lässt mit Botschaft.
Ich soll sehr schnell
Herbei und Ihn in einer üblen Lage soutenieren,
In die Er unverschuldter Weise geraten ist!

BARON *(greift sich an den Kopf)*.

KOMMISSARIUS: Wer ist der Herr? Was schafft der Herr mit Ihm?

BARON: Nichts von Bedeutung. Ist bloss ein Bekannter,
hält sich per Zufall hier im Gasthaus auf.

KOMMISSARIUS: Der Herr geb' seinen Namen an!

FANINAL: Ich bin der Edle von Faninal.

KOMMISSARIUS: Ja, ja, genügt schon.

                                 (Zu Faninal.)

Er erkennt demnach
in diesem Herrn hier Seinen Schwiegersohn?

FANINAL: Sehr wohl! Wie sollt' ich Ihn nicht erkennen?
Leicht, weil Er keine Haar nicht hat?

KOMMISSARIUS *(zum Baron)*:

Und Er erkennt nunmehr wohl auch in diesem Herrn
Wohl oder übel Seinen Schwiegervater?

BARON *(nimmt den Leuchter vom Tisch, beleuchtet sich Faninal genau)*:

So so, la la! Ja, ja, wird schon derselbe sein.
War heut den ganzen Abend gar nicht recht beinand,
Kann meinen Augen heut nicht traun. Muss Ihm sagen,
Liegt hier was in der Luft, man kriegt die Kongestion
                                 davon

KOMMISSARIUS *(zum Faninal)*:

Dagegen wird von Ihm die Vaterschaft
zu dieser Ihm verbatim zugeschobenen Tochter
Geleugnet.

FANINAL *(bemerkt jetzt erst Octavian)*:
Meine Tochter?

(The servants of the inn, other guests, also some of the musicians from the next room have crowded around the door and look in curiously. Herr von Faninal forces his way through the crowd, much perturbed, in hat and cloak.)

FANINAL: The same, Sir. What might you desire of me?

               (Goes to the Baron.)

Why, how you look,
I scarce expected you would need my presence
At this untimely hour, here in a common pot-house.

BARON *(very much surprised and annoyed)*:
And who asked you to meddle, in the name of mischief?

FANINIAL: Why ask such questions, like a fool, Sir son-in-law,
When messengers from you came batt'ring at my house-
              door
And shouting I must come in hottest haste to rescue you
           from gravest danger,
Which by no fault of yours was threatening your liberty.

     (The Baron seizes his head in his hand.)

COMMISSARY: Whom have we here? What is your talk with him?

BARON: 'Tis nothing—nothing. We are scarce acquainted—
'Tis but a chance that he is staying here.

COMMISSARY *(to Faninal)*:
Your name—and tell me why you're here.

FANINAL: I am the Baron of Faninal.

COMMISSARY: Yes, yes, I follow. Then you recognize
This gentleman for your son-in-law?

FANINAL: For sure; how should I fail to recognize him?
Maybe because his pate is bald?

COMMISSARY *(to the Baron)*:
And you now recognize this gentleman to be
For good or evil, the young lady's father?

BARON *(taking the candlestick from the table and holding it up to Faninal's face)*.
So, so! La, la! Yes, yes! May be that it is he—
My head to-day has been quite giddy and confused—
I can no longer trust my eyes. I feel
There's here a something in the air that gives a man a
             fever'd brain.

COMMISSARY *(to Faninal)*:
You on the other hand deny you are
The father of this girl here who is said
To be your daughter?

FANINAL *(now for the first time noticing Octavian)*:
That my daughter?

Meine Tochter soll herauf!
Sitzt unten in der Tragchaise. Im Galopp herauf!

(*Wieder auf den Baron losstürzend.*)
Das zahlt Er teuer! Bring' Ihn vors Gericht!

BARON (*im Wilden Herumfahren, um die Perücke zu suchen, fasst er einige der Kinder an und stösst sie zur Seite*).

DIE KINDER (*automatisch*):
Papa! Papa! Papa!

FANINAL (*fährt zurück*):
Was ist denn das?

BARON (*im Suchen findet wenigstens seinen Hut, schlägt mit aem Hut nach den Kindern*):
Gar nix, ein Schwindel! Kenn' nit das Bagagi!
Sie sagt, dass sie verheirat' war mit mir.
Käm' zu der Schand', so wie der Pontius ins credo!

SOPHIE (*kommt im Mantel eilig herein, man macht ihr Platz. An der Tür sieht man die Faninalschen Bedienten, jeder eine Tragstange der Sänfte haltend. Baron sucht die Kahlheit seines Kopfs vor Sophie mit dem Hut zu beschatten*).

VIELE STIMMEN (*indes Sophie auf ihren Vater zugeht, dumpf*):
Da ist die Braut. Oh was für ein Skandal!

DUMPFE STIMMEN: Der Skandal! Der Skandal!
Fürn Herrn von Faninal!

FANINAL: Da! Aus dem Keller! Aus der Luft! Die ganze Wiener-
stadt!
(*Auf den Baron zu, mit geballter Faust.*)
Oh, Er Filou! Mir wird nicht gut! Ein' Sessel!
(*Bediente springen hinzu, fangen ihn auf. Zwei desgleichen haben vorher ihre Stange einem der Hinterstehenden zugeworfen. Sophie ist angstvoll um ihn bemüht. Wirt springt gleichfalls hinzu. Sie nehmen ihn auf und tragen ihn ins Nebenzimmer. Mehrere Kellner den Weg weisend, die Türe öffnend voran. Baron wird diesem Augenblick seiner Perücke ansichtig, die wie durch Zauberhand wieder zum Vorschein gekommen ist, stürzt darauf los, stülpt sie sich auf und gibt ihr vor dem Spiegel den richtigen Sitz. Mit dieser Veränderung gewinnt er seine Haltung so ziemlich wieder, begnügt sich aber, Annina und den Kindern, deren Rücken zu kehren. Hinte. Herrn von Faninal und seiner Begleitung hat sich die Türe links geschlossen. Wirt und Kellner kommen bald darauf leise wieder heraus, holen Medikamente, Karaffen mit Wasser und anderes, das in die Tür getragen und von Sophie in der Türspalte übernommen wird.*)

Summon my daughter here. She waits in her sedan-
chair—
Bid her come up at once.
(Again going to the Baron.)
You'll pay this dearly! I will go to law!

BARON: What mighty pother you are making
About a little thing—To be your son-in-law a man must
have
The patience of an ass, parole d'honneur!
Now bring my wig here!
(Shakes the Landlord.)
Find my wig! Find me my wig!

*(In his wild hunt for his wig, he seizes some of the children and
pushes them aside.)*

THE FOUR CHILDREN *(automatically)*:
Papa! Papa! Papa!

FANINAL *(starts back)*:
What brats are those?

BARON *(in his wild search he has come across his hat and hits out at
the children with it)*:
Nothing! A lie! Till now I never saw her!
She says that she's my lawful wedded wife!
Heav'n only knows why things like this are sent to try us!

*(At the door appear servants of Faninal, each one holding the
pole of a sedan-chair. Sophia comes in in hat and cloak. All
make room for her. The Baron tries to conceal his bald pate
from Sophia with his hat, while Sophia goes towards her father.)*
CHORUS: The bride! Oh, what a sad disgrace!

MUFFLED VOICES FROM ALL SIDES:
A disgrace! A disgrace!
For him and all his race!

FANINAL: From the cellar! From the air! I dare not show my
face—
(Going towards the Baron with clenched fist.)
The villain! I am not well! An armchair!
*(His servants run forward and save him from falling. Two of them
had already given their poles to the onlookers. Sophia hurries
to his aid. They lift him up and carry him to the next room.
Several waiters precede them, showing the way and opening the
door. At this moment the Baron is aware of his wig, which has
reappeared, as if by magic, darts towards it, clasps it on his pate
and, going to a mirror, sets it straight. With this change he
regains some of his lost self-confidence, but satisfies himself
with turning his back on Annina and the Children, whose presence, after all, he regards with uneasiness.)*
*(The door to the left is closed behind Herr von Faninal and his
following. The waiters and the Landlord after a time emerge
quietly and go to fetch drugs, bottles with water and other things,
which they carry as far as the door and hand to Sophia through
the opening.)*

BARON (*nunmehr mit dem alten Selbstgefühl auf den Kommissarius zu*):
Sind desto ehr im Klaren. Ich zahl', ich geh'!

(*Zu Octavian.*)
Ich führ' Sie jetzt nach Haus.

KOMMISSARIUS: Da irrt Er sich. Mit Ihm jetzt weiter im Verhör!

(*Auf den Wink des Kommissarius entfernen die beiden Wächter
alle übrigen Personen aus dem Zimmer, nur Annina mit den
Kindern bleibt an der linken Wand stehen.*)

OCTAVIAN: Herr Kommissar, i geb' was zu Protokoll,
Aber der Herr Baron darf nicht zuhörn dabei.

(*Auf den Wink des Kommissarius drängen die beiden Wächter den
Baron nach vorne rechts. Octavian scheint dem Kommissarius
etwas zu melden, was diesen sehr überrascht.*)

BARON (*zu den Wächtern, familiär, halblaut, auf Annina hindeutend*):
Kenn' nicht das Weibsbild dort, auf Ehr'. War grad'
beim Essen!
Hab' keine Ahnung, was sie will. Hätt' sonst nicht selber
um die Polizei —

(*Der Kommissarius begleitet Octavian bis an den Alkoven. Octavian
verschwindet hinter dem Vorhang. Der Kommissarius scheint
sich zu amüsieren und ist den Spalten des Vorhangs ungenierter-
weise nahe.*)

BARON (*bemerkt die Heiterkeit des Kommissarius, plötzlich sehr auf-
geregt über den unerklärlichen Vorfall*):
Was g'schieht denn dort? Is wohl nich möglich das? Der
Lackl!
Das heisst Ihr Sittenpolizei? Ist eine Jungfer!

(*Er ist schwer zu halten.*)
Steht unter meiner Protektion! Beschwer' mich!
Hab' da ein Wörtel drein zu reden!

(*Reisst sich los, will gegen das Bett hin. Sie fangen und halten ihn
wieder. Aus dem Alkoven erscheinen Stück für Stück die Kleider
der Mariandel. Der Kommissarius macht ein Bündel daraus.*)

BARON (*immer aufgeregt, ringt, seine beiden Wächter los zu werden*):
Muss jetzt partout zu ihr!

(*Sie halten ihn mühsam, während Octavians Kopf aus einer Spalte
des Vorhangs hervorsieht.*)

WIRT (*hereinstürmend*):
Ihre hochfürstliche Gnaden, die Frau Fürstin Feldmarschallin!

(*Kellner herein, reissen die Türe auf. Zuerst werden einige Menschen in der Marschallin Livree sichtbar, sie rangieren sich, Marschallin tritt ein, der kleine Neger trägt ihre Schleppe.*)

BARON (*going towards the Commissary with self-confidence now* **fully** *restored*) :

>This clears our path but the sooner.
>I pay, and go.

> (*To Octavian.*)

>And you I'll now take home.

COMMISSARY: Pray, not so fast. A few more questions ere you go—

(*At a sign from the Commissary, the Constables remove from the room everybody except Annina and the Children, who remain standing by the wall to the left.*

OCTAVIAN (*speaking*) :

>I have something that I would say to the Officer
>Gentleman, but the Baron must not listen.

(*At a sign from the Commissary the two Constables shepherd the Baron to the front of the stage to the right. Octavian says something to the Commissary which seems to surprise him very much. The Commissary accompanies him to the recess and he disappears behind the curtain.*)

BARON (*familiarly to the Constables, pointing to Annina*) :

>I ne'er did see that slut till now. We were at supper—
>I have no inkling what she seeks.

(*The Commissary seems to be vastly entertained and unconcernedly approaches the open curtain.*)

BARON : Else would I surely not have asked your aid.

>(*Suddenly much perturbed at the inexplicable proceeding.*)
>What is happening there? Can I believe my eyes?
>The scoundrel! Look! He too, who dared to threaten

> me !

>It is an outrage, yes, an outrage!

> (*They have difficulty in holding him back.*)

>She's under my protection. I warn you,
>You'll smart for this behaviour.

(*He makes himself free and goes towards the recess; they pursue him and seize him again. From the recess are thrown Mariandel's clothes, piece by piece. The Commissary makes a bundle of them. The Baron struggles with his captors. They hold him with difficulty, while Octavian puts his head out of the opening of the curtains.*)

LANDLORD (*rushes in*) :

>The Princess, her Highness the Princess of Werdenberg.

(*First some men in the Princess's livery appear, then the Baron's Body Servant. They form a line. Then the Princess enters, the Little Black Boy carrying her train. The Baron has shaken* **off his captors, mops his forehead and hurries towards the Princess.**)

BARON (*hat sich von den Wächtern losgerissen, wischt sich den Schweiss von der Stirne, eilt auf die Marschallin zu*):

> Bin glücklich über Massen, hab' die Gnad' kaum meritiert,
> Schätz' Dero Gegenwart hier als ein Freundstück ohne-
> gleichen.

OCTAVIAN (*streckt den Kopf zwischen dem Vorhang hervor*):

> Marie Theres', wie kommt Sie her?

(*Marschallin regungslos, antwortet nicht, sieht sich fragend um.*)

KOMMISSARIUS (*auf die Fürstin zu, in dienstlicher Haltung*):

> Fürstliche Gnaden, melde mich gehorsamst
> Als vorstädtischer Unterkommissarius.

BARON (*gleichzeitig*):

> Er sieht, Herr Kommissar, die Durchlaucht haben selber
>   sich bemüht.
> Ich denk', Er weiss, woran Er ist.

(*Leiblakai auf den Baron zu, stolz und selbstzufrieden. Baron winkt ihm als Zeichen seiner Zufriedenheit.*)

MARSCHALLIN (*zum Kommissar, ohne den Baron zu beachten*):

> Er kennt mich? Kenn' ich Ihn nicht auch? Mir scheint
>   beinah'.

KOMMISSARIUS: Sehr wohl.

MARSCHALLIN: Dem Herrn Feldmarschall seine brave Ordonanz gewest?

KOMMISSARIUS: Fürstliche Gnaden, zu Befehl!

(*Octavian steckt abermals den Kopf zwischen den Vorhängen hervor.*)

BARON (*winkt ihm heftig, zu verschwinden, ist zugleich ängstlich bemüht, dass die Marschallin nichts merkte. Halblaut*):

> Bleib' Sie, zum Sakra, hinten dort!

(*Dann hört er, wie sich Schritte der Tür links vorne nähern; stürzt hin, stellt sich mit dem Rücken gegen die Türe, durch verbind-liche Gebärden gegen die Marschallin bestrebt, seinem Gehaben den Schein völliger Unbefangenheit zu geben.*)

MARSCHALLIN (*kommt gegen links, mit zuwartender Miene den Baron anblickend*).

OCTAVIAN (*in Männerkleidung tritt zwischen den Vorhängen hervor, sobald der Baron ihm den Rücken kehrt; halblaut*):

> War anders abgemacht! Marie Theres', ich wunder' mich!

MARSCHALLIN (*als hörte sie ihn nicht, hat fortwährend den verbindlich erwartungsvollen Blick auf den Baron gerichtet, der in äusserster Verlegenheit zwischen der Tür und der Marschallin seine Auf merksamkeit teilt. Die Tür links wird mit Kraft geöffnet, so dass der Baron der vergebens versucht hatte, sich dagegen zu stemmen, wütend zurückzutreten genötigt ist. Zwei Faninals Diener lassen jetzt Sophie eintreten*).

BARON: Your Highness overwhelms me. This is more than I
                                                    deserve.
           Your presence, here, your Highness, does betoken truest
                                                    friendship.

OCTAVIAN (*his head appearing behind the curtain*):

           Marie Theres'! How came you here?

(*The Princess stands motionless and does not answer. She looks
round with a questioning glance.*)

(*The Body Servant, proud and pleased with himself, goes towards
the Baron. The Baron gives him signs of his satisfaction.*)

COMMISSARY (*going towards the Princess, at attention*):

           May't please your Highness, my most humble duty.
           The Commissary of this district.

BARON   Her Highness, as you see, has deigned to come in person
                                                    to my aid.
           And now perhaps you'll know the man I am.

PRINCESS: You know me? Do I know you too? I almost think.—

COMMISSARY: Right well.

PRINCESS: Were you not long ago the Prince Field Marshal's orderly?

COMMISSARY: 'Tis so, your highness, to command.
                      (*Octavian again puts his head through the curtains.*)
           (*The Baron makes a sign to Octavian to vanish, and is at the same
           time in great anxiety lest the Princess should observe him.*)

BARON: Plague on you, stay there! Hide yourself.

(*The Baron hears steps approaching the door on the left to the front,
rushes there and places himself with his back to the door, trying
by means of gestures in the direction of the Princess to appear
quite at his ease. The Princess steps towards the left and looks
at the Baron expectantly. Octavian comes from behind the cus-
tain, in male clothes, as soon as the Baron has turned his back.*)

OCTAVIAN: It was not this we hoped! Marie Theres', I wonder much!

(*The Princess, as though not hearing Octavian, fixes a courteous
expectant look on the Baron, who in the utmost perplexity is divid-
ing his attention between the Princess and the door. The door
on the left is opened violently, so that the Baron, who has been
leaning against it in a vain attempt to keep it closed, is pushed
forward. Two of Faninal's servants now stand aside to let
Sophia pass.*)

SOPHIE (*ohne die Marschallin zu sehen, die ihr durch den Baron verdeckt ist*):

Hab' ihm von mei'm Herrn Vater zu vermelden!

BARON (*ihr ins Wort fallend, halblaut*):

Is jetzo nicht die Zeit, Kreuzelement!
Kann Sie nicht warten, bis dass man Ihr rufen wird?
Meint Sie, dass ich Sie hier im Beisl präsentieren werd'?

OCTAVIAN (*ist leise hervorgetretten, zur Marschallin, halblaut*):

Das ist die Fräulein — die — um derentwillen —

MARSCHALLIN (*über die Schulter zu Octavian halblaut*):

Find' Ihn ein bissl empressiert, Rofrano.
Kann mir wohl denken, wer sie ist. Find' sie scharmant.
(*Octavian schlüpft zwischen die Vorhänge zurück.*)

SOPHIE (*den Rücken gegen die Türe, so scharf, dass der Baron unwillkürlich einen Schritt zurückweicht*):

Er wird mich keinem Menschen auf der Welt nicht präsentieren,
Dieweilen ich mit Ihm auch nicht so viel zu schaffen hab.
(*Die Marschallin spricht leise mit dem Kommissar.*)
Und mein Herr Vater lasst Ihm sagen: wenn Er alsoweit
Die Frechheit sollte treiben, dass man seine Nasen nur
Erblicken tät' auf hundert Schritt von unserm Stadtpalais,
So hätt' Er sich die bösen Folgen selber zuzuschreiben,
Das ist, was mein Herr Vater Ihm vermelden lässt.

BARON (*zornig*):

Corpo di bacco!
Was ist das für eine ungezogene Sprach'!

SOPHIE: Die Ihm gebührt.

BARON (*ausser sich, will an ihr vorbei, zur Tür hinein*):

He, Faninal, ich muss —

SOPHIE: Er untersteh' sich nicht!

(*Die zwei Faninalschen Diener treten hervor, halten ihn auf, schieben ihn zurück. Sophie tritt in die Tür, die sich hinter ihr schliesst.*)

BARON (*gegen die Tür brüllend*):

Bin willens, alles Vorgefall'ne
Vergeben und vergessen sein zu lassen!

MARSCHALLIN (*ist von rückwärts an den Baron herangetreten und klopft ihm auf die Schulter*):

Lass' Er nur gut sein und verschwind' Er auf eins zwei!

BARON (*dreht sich um, starrt sie an*):

Wieso denn?

MARSCHALLIN (*munter, überlegen*):

Wahr' Er sein Dignité und fahr' Er ab!

BARON (*sprachlos*):

Ich? Was?

SOPHIA (*without seeing the Princess, who is hidden from her by the Baron*):

I have to bring you a message from my father . . .

BARON (*interrupting her, in an undertone*):

'Tis most untimely now, can you not wait!
Can you not wait until the proper time has come?
Think you this pothouse here is fitting for an introduction?

OCTAVIAN (*who now comes quietly from the recess, aside to the Princess*):

That is the lady—who—to whom you sent me—

PRINCESS (*aside to Octavian, over her shoulder*):

Surely there's here a little haste, Rofrano.
'Tis easy guessing who she is. Your taste is good.

(*Octavian slips back behind the curtain.*)

SOPHIA (*her back to the door, so angrily that the Baron instinctively starts back a step*):

You will not here, nor anywhere, to anyone present me,
Know that from henceforth I have done with you once
and for all.

(*The Princess converses in a low voice with the Commissary.*)

And this my father bids me tell you: should you ever
So far carry your presumption, as to dare to let your face
Be seen within a hundred yards of where our mansion is,
You'll have yourself alone to thank for all that may befall
you.
That is the message that my father sends to you.

BARON (*very angrily*):

Corpo di Bacco!
What impertinence is this, what ill-bred language?

SOPHIA: 'Tis your desert.

BARON (*beside himself, tries to pass her and reach the door*):

Ha, Faninal, I must—

SOPHIA: Stand back, Sir! Do not dare!

(*The two footmen of Faninal come forward, bar his passage and push him back. Sophia passes out. The door is closed behind her.*)

BARON (*shouting against the door*):

I am content that all that's happened
Shall henceforth be forgiven and forgotten.

(*The Princess approaches the Baron from behind and taps him on the shoulder.*)

PRINCESS: Leave well alone, and ere I count to three, withdraw!

(*The Baron turns round and stares at her.*)

BARON: What mean you?

PRINCESS (*gaily, sure of victory*):

Think of your dignity and take your leave!

BARON (*speechless*):

I? How?

MARSCHALLIN: Mach Er bonne mine à mauvais jeu:
So bleibt Er quasi doch noch eine Standsperson.

BARON (*starrt sie stumm an*).
(*Sophie tritt leise wieder heraus. Ihre Augen suchen Octavian.*)

MARSCHALLIN (*zum Kommissar, der hinten rechts steht, desgleichen seine Wächter*):
Er sieht, Herr Kommissar:
das Ganze war halt eine Farce und weiter nichts.

KOMMISSARIUS: Genügt mir! Retirier' mich ganz gehorsamst.
(*Tritt ab, die beiden Wächter hinter ihm.*)

SOPHIE (*vor sich, erschrocken*):
Das Ganze war halt eine Farce und weiter nichts .
(*Die Blicke der beiden Frauen begegnen sich; Sophie macht der Marschallin einen verlegnen Knicks.*)

BARON (*zwischen Sophie und der Marschallin stehend*):
Bin gar nicht willens!

MARSCHALLIN (*ungeduldig, stampft auf*):
Mon Cousin, bedeut' Er Ihm!
(*Kehrt dem Baron den Rücken.*)

OCTAVIAN (*geht von rückwärts auf den Baron zu, sehr männlich*):
Möcht Ihn sehr bitten!

BARON (*fährt herum*):
Wer? Was?

MARSCHALLIN (*von rechts, wo sie nun steht*):
Sein' Gnaden, der Herr Graf Rofrano, wer denn sonst?

BARON (*nachdem er sich Octavians Gesicht scharf und in der Nähe betrachtet, mit Resignation*):
Is schon a so!
(*Vor sich.*)
Hab' g'nug von dem Gesicht,
Sind doch nicht meine Augen schuld. Is schon ein Mandl.
(*Octavian steht frech und hochmütig da.*)

MARSCHALLIN (*einen Schritt näher tretend*):
Ist eine wienerische Maskerad' und weiter nichts.

SOPHIE (*halb traurig, halb höhnisch für sich*):
Ist eine wienerische Maskerad' und weiter nichts.

BARON (*sehr vor den Kopf geschlagen*):
Aha!
(*Für sich.*)
Spiel'n alle unter einem Leder gegen meiner!

MARSCHALLIN (*von oben herab*):
Ich hätt' Ihm nicht gewunschen,
Dass Er mein Mariandl in der Wirklichkeit mir hätte debauchiert!

PRINCESS: If you would still preserve your name
As gentleman, make virtue of necessity.

(The Baron stares at her in speechless amazement. Sophia again comes quietly out of the other room. Her eyes seek Octavian.)

PRINCESS *(to the Commissary, who is standing at the back on the right with the two Constables)*:
And now, 'tis all quite clear;
It all has been just a diversion—nothing more.

COMMISSARY: Enough! I humbly beg leave to withdraw.
(Exit, followed by the two Constables.)

SOPHIA *(aside, afraid)*:
The whole has been just a diversion—nothing more.

(The eyes of the two women meet; Sophia makes an embarrassed curtsey.)

BARON *(standing between Sophia and the Princess)*:
Not so, your Highness!

PRINCESS *(impatiently, stamping her foot)*:
Mon cousin, explain to him!

(Turns her back on the Baron.)

OCTAVIAN *(approaches the Baron from behind. Very mannish)*:
Will you permit me?

BARON *(turns on him sharply)*:
Who? What?

PRINCESS *(on the right, where she now takes up her position)*:
The Count Rofrano, my dear kinsman, who but he?

BARON *(resignedly, after careful scrutiny of Octavian's face)*:
I thought as much!
(To himself.)
That face, I'm sick of it,
My eyes did not mislead me then. For sure, 'twas he.
(Octavian stands there, arrogant and defiant.)

PRINCESS *(approaching a step nearer)*:
A masquerade, as we in Vienna practise,—nothing more.

SOPHIA *(half sadly, half ironically to herself)*:
A masquerade, as we in Vienna practise,—nothing more.

BARON *(greatly amazed)*:
Aha!
(To himself.)
I see now they are all conspiring to befool me!

PRINCESS *(haughtily)*:
'Tis well for you it was not
Really my Mariandel whom you villainous persuasions have
misled!

(Baron as before deep in thought.)

BARON (*wie oben, vor sich hin sinnierend*).

MARSCHALLIN (*wie oben und ohne Octavian anzusehen*):
    Hab' jetzt einen montierten Kopf gegen die Männer —
    so ganz im allgemeinen!

BARON (*allmählich der Situation beikommend*):
    Kreuzelement! Komm' aus dem Staunen nicht heraus!
    Der Feldmarschall — Octavian — Mariandl — die Marschal-
                         lin — Octavian.
  (*Mit einem ausgiebigen Blick, der von Marschallin zu Octavian, von
  Octavian wieder zurück zur Marschallin wandert.*)
    Weiss bereits nicht, was ich von diesem ganzen qui-pro-
                                 quo
    mir denken soll!

MARSCHALLIN (*mit einem langen Blick, dann mit grosser Sicherheit*):
    Er ist, mein' ich, ein Kavalier? Da wird Er sich halt gar
                              nichts denken.
    Das ist's, was ich von Ihm erwart'.
                                   (*Pause.*)

BARON (*mit Verneigung und weltmännisch*):
    Bin von so viel Finesse scharmiert, kann gar nicht sagen,
                                 wie.
    Ein Lerchenauer war noch nie kein Spielverderber nicht.
               (*Einen Schritt an sie herantretend.*)
    Find' deliziös das ganze qui-pro-quo,
    bedarf aber dafür nunmehro Ihrer Protektion.
    Bin willens, alles Vorgefallene
    vergeben und vergessen sein zu lassen.
                                  (*Pause.*)
    Eh bien, darf ich den Faninal —
        (*Er macht Miene, an die Türe links zu gehen.*)

MARSCHALLIN: Er darf — Er darf in aller Still' sich retirieren.

BARON (*aus allen Himmeln gefallen*).

MARSCHALLIN: Versteht Er nicht, wenn eine Sach' ein End' hat?
    Die ganze Brautschaft und Affär' und alles sonst.
    Was drum und dran hängt,
                        (*sehr bestimmt*)
    Ist mit dieser Stund' vorbei.

SOPHIE (*sehr betreten, für sich*):
    Was drum und dran hängt, ist mit dieser Stund vorbei!

BARON (*für sich, empört, halblaut*):
    Mit dieser Stund' vorbei! Mit dieser Stund' vorbei

MARSCHALLIN (*scheint sich nach einem Stuhl umzusehen, Octavian springt
    hin, gibt ihr einen Stuhl. Marschallin setzt sich rechts, mit Be-
    deutung für sich*):
    Ist halt vorbei.

PRINCESS (*as before and without looking at Octavian*):
>I feel just now a bitter grudge, a deep resentment
>Against all men in general!

BARON (*gradually realizing the situation*):
>God bless my soul! I'm in a maze without a clue!

(*With a comprehensive glance which wanders from the Princess to Octavian and from Octavian back to the Princess.*)
>In all this crazy comedy I'm at a loss to know
>What I should think.

PRINCESS (*looking at him fixedly, then emphatically*):
>It best befits a gentleman in such case to refrain from
>>thinking.
>That is what I expect of you.

BARON (*with a bow and the manner of a man of the world*):
>Sure, sentiments so exquisite with admiration fill me quite.
>And none could ever say of any Lerchenau that he would
>>spoil good sport.

>>>(*Approaching the Princess.*)

>I find this whole diversion vastly droll,
>But in return I need your Highness's help and interest.
>I am content to let these incidents
>And all that's passed from henceforth be forgotten.

>>>(*Pause.*)

>Eh bien, may I tell Faninal—

>>>(*Approaching the door to the left.*)

PRINCESS: You may—you may say nothing, and so leave us.

>>>(*The Baron is thunderstruck with surprise.*)

PRINCESS: Do you not know when you can go no further?
>Your great alliance and whate'er it means both now
>And in the future

>>>(*Emphatically.*)

>From this hour you must renounce.

SOPHIA (*in great astonishment, aside*):
>His great alliance from this hour he must renounce.

BARON (*aside, indignantly, softly*):
>From now I must renounce! From now I must renounce!

PRINCESS (*seems to look for a chair. Octavian hurries forward and gives her one. The Princess takes a seat to the right and says significantly, aside*):
>I must renounce!

SOPHIE (*links vor sich, blass*):
Ist halt vorbei!

(*Baron findet sich durchaus nicht in diese Wendung, rollt verlegen und aufgebracht die Augen. In diesem Augenblick kommt der Mann aus der Falltür hervor. Von links tritt Valzacchi ein, die Verdächtigen in bescheidener Haltung hinter ihm. Annina nimmt Witwenhaube und Schleier ab, wischt sich die Schminke weg und zeigt ihr gewöhnliches Gesicht. Dies alles zu immer gesteigertem Staunen des Barons. Der Wirt, eine lange Rechnung in der Hand, tritt zur Mitteltüre herein, hinter ihm Kellner, Musikanten, Hausknechte, Kutscher.*)

BARON (*wie er sie alle erblickt, gibt er sein Spiel verloren. Ruft schnell entschlossen*):
Leupold, wir gehn!

(*Macht der Marschallin ein tiefes, aber zorniges Kompliment. Leiblakai ergreift einen Leuchter vom Tisch und will seinem Herrn voran.*)

ANNINA (*stellt sich frech dem Baron in den Weg*):
„Ich hab' halt schon einmal ein Lerchenauisch Glück."
(*Auf die Rechnung des Wirtes deutend.*)
„Komm' Sie nach Tisch, geb' Ihr die Antwort nachher
schriftlich!"

(*Die Kinder kommen dem Baron unter die Füsse. Er schlägt mit dem Hut unter sie.*)

DIE KINDER: Papa! Papa! Papa!

KELLNER (*sich zuerst an den Baron drängend*):
Entschuld'gen Euer Gnaden!
Uns gehen die Kerzen an!

WIRT (*sich mit der Rechnung vordrängend*):
Entschuld'gen Euer Gnaden!

ANNINA (*vor dem Baron her nach rückwärts tanzend*):
„Ich hab' halt schon einmal ein Lerchenauisch Glück!"

VALZACCHI (*höhnisch*):
„Ich hab' halt schon einmal ein Lerchenauisch Glück!"

DIE MUSIKANTEN (*sich dem Baron in dem Weg stellend*):
Tafelmusik über zwei Stunden!

LEIBLAKAI (*bahnt sich den Weg gegen die Tür hin*).

BARON (*will hinter ihm durch*).

DIE KUTSCHER (*auf den Baron eindringend*):
Für die Fuhr', für die Fuhr,' Rösser g'schund'n ham ma
gnua!
HAUSKNECHT (*den Baron grob anrempelnd*):
Sö fürs Aufsperrn, Sö, Herr Baron!

SOPHIA (*on the left, pale*) :
>   He must renounce.

(*The Baron finds it difficult to realize the new developments and rolls his eyes in anger and perplexity. In this moment the man emerges from the trap-door. Valzacchi enters from the left, his suspicious accomplices following him. Annina takes off her widow's cap and veil, wipes off the paint and shows her natural face. The Baron watches this in growing astonishment. The Landlord carrying a long bill in his hand enters by the centre door, followed by the Waiters, Musicians, Boots and Coachmen.*)

BARON (*when he sees this knows that his game is lost, calls out quickly and decidedly*) :
>   Leopold, we go!

(*Makes a deep but angry bow to the Princess. His Body Servant takes a candle from the table and precedes his master.*)

ANNINA (*insolently bars the Baron's passage*) :
>   "For sure I have the luck of all the Lerchenaus."
>
>   (*Pointing to the Landlord with his bill.*)
>
>   "Come when I've dined, I'll give the answer then in
>   writing."

(*The Children run between the Baron's legs. He hits out at them with his hat.*)

CHILDREN :   Papa! Papa! Papa!

WAITERS (*pressing round the Baron*) :
>   May it please you, your Lordship,
>   Item, the candlelight!

LANDLORD (*pressing forward with his bill*) :
>   May it please you your Lordship.

ANNINA (*dancing backwards in front of the Baron*) :
>   "I surely have the luck of all the Lerchenaus!"

VALZACCHI (*ironically*) :
>   "I surely have the luck of all the Lerchenaus!"

MUSICIANS (*coming in front of the Baron*) :
>   Item, music two hours and over.

(*The Body Servant forces a passage to the door. The Baron tries to follow him.*)

COACHMEN (*pressing round the Baron*) :
>   Coach hire, coach hire! Our poor horses whipped to death!

BOOTS (*insolently shouting at the Baron*) :
>   For opening the doors, your Lordship!

WIRT (*immer die Rechnung präsentierend*) :
　　　　　Entschuld'gen Euer Gnaden.

KELLNER: 　　Zwei Schock Kerzen, uns gehen die Kerzen **an**.

BARON (*im Gedränge*) :
　　　　　Platz da, zurück da, Kreuzmillion.

DIE KINDER: Papa! Papa! Papa!

ALLE (*schreien wild durcheinander*).

BARON (*drängt sich mit Macht durch gegen die Ausgangstür, alle dicht
　　　　　um ihn in einem Knäuel*).

HAUSKNECHT: Führa g'fahr'n, aussa g'ruckt, Sö. Herr Baron!

ALLE (*sind schon in der Tür, dem Lakai wird der Armleuchter ent-
　　　　　wunden*).

BARON (*stürzt ab*).

ALLE (*stürmen ihm nach, der Lärm verhallt. Die zwei Faninalschen
　　　　　Diener sind indessen links abgetreten. Es bleiben allein zurück:
　　　　　Sophie, die Marschallin und Octavian*).

SOPHIE (*links stehend, blass*) :
　　　　　Mein Gott, es war nicht mehr als eine Farce.
　　　　　Mein Gott, mein Gott!
　　　　　Wie Er bei ihr steht und ich bin die leere Luft für Ihn.

OCTAVIAN (*hinter dem Stuhl der Marschallin verlegen*) :
　　　　　War anders abgemacht, Marie Theres', ich wunder' mich.
　　　　　　　　　　(*In höchster Verlegenheit.*)
　　　　　Befiehlt Sie, dass ich — soll ich nicht — die Jungfer — der
　　　　　　　　　　　　　　　　　　　Vater —

MARSCHALLIN: Geh' Er doch schnell und tu' Er, was sein Herz Ihm sagt.

SOPHIE (*verzweifelt*) :
　　　　　Die leere Luft. O mein Gott, o mein Gott!

OCTAVIAN: 　　Theres', ich weiss gar nicht —

MARSCHALLIN: Geh' Er und mach' Er seinen Hof.

OCTAVIAN: 　　Ich schwör Ihr —

MARSCHALLIN: Lass Er's gut sein.

OCTAVIAN: 　　Ich begreif' nicht, was Sie hat.

MARSCHALLIN (*lacht zornig*) :
　　　　　Er ist ein rechtes Mannsbild, geh' Er hin.

OCTAVIAN: 　　Was Sie befiehlt.
　　　　　　　　　　　　　　　(*Geht hinüber.*)
SOPHIE (*wortlos*).

OCTAVIAN (*bei ihr*) :
　　　　　Eh bien, hat Sie kein freundlich Wort für mich?
　　　　　Nicht einen Blick, nicht einen lieben Gruss?

LANDLORD (*still presenting his bill*) :
         May it please you, your Lordship.

WAITERS :   Two score candles, item, the candlelight!

BARON (*in the middle of the crowd*) :
         Make room, make room, deuce take you all!

CHILDREN :   Papa! Papa! Papa!
    (*The Baron struggles violently towards the door, all follow him in confusion.*)

BOOTS :   I am the boots, that opened the doors, may it please your
                                       Loɪdship!
    (*The whole crowd is in the doorway, someone wrests the candlestick from the Body Servant. The Baron rushes off. All tear after him. The noise grows fainter. Faninal's two Footmen have in the meanwhile gone through the door on the left. Sophia, Princess and Octavian are left alone.*)

SOPHIA (*standing on left, pale*) :
         The whole affair has been a mere diversion
         And nothing more—
         How he leans o'er her, and I am but as empty air for him.

OCTAVIAN (*behind the Princess's chair, embarrassed*) :
         It was not thus we hoped, Marie Theres'—I stand amazed—
                        (*In extreme perplexity.*)
         Perchance you wish it. . . . Shall I not. . . . The
                lady. . . . Her father. . . .

PRINCESS :   Go quickly, go, and do all that your heart commands.

SOPHIA (*in despair*) :
         But empty air! O help me, gracious Heav'n!

OCTAVIAN :   Theres', I have no words!

PRINCESS :   Woo her and win her love—

OCTAVIAN :   I wonder—

PRINCESS :   'Tis no matter—

OCTAVIAN :   On my honour, what you mean—

PRINCESS (*laughs angrily*) :
         How like the rest! How manlike! Go to her!

OCTAVIAN :   As you command!
                    (*Crosses to Sophia, who stands silent.*)
         Eh bien, have you no kindly word for me?
         No smile, no look, no greeting, not one sign?

SOPHIE (*stockend*):
       War mir von Euer Gnaden Freundschaft und Behilflich-
                                     keit
       Wahrhaftig einer andern Freud' gewärtig.

OCTAVIAN (*lebhaft*):
       Wie — freut Sie sich denn nicht?

SOPHIE (*unmutig*):
       Hab' wirklich keinen Anlass nicht.

OCTAVIAN: Hat man Ihr nicht den Bräutigam vom Hals geschafft?

SOPHIE: Wär' all's recht schön, wenn's anders abgegangen wär'.
       Schäm mich in Grund und Boden. Versteh' sehr wohl,
       Mit was für einen Blick Ihre fürstliche Gnaden mich
                               betracht'.

OCTAVIAN: Ich schwör Ihr, meiner Seel' und Seligkeit.

SOPHIE: Lass Er mich gehn.

OCTAVIAN: Ich lass Sie nicht.
                              (*Fasst ihre Hand.*)

SOPHIE: Der Vater braucht mich drin.

OCTAVIAN: Ich brauch' Sie nötiger.

SOPHIE: Das sagt sich leicht.

OCTAVIAN: Ich hab' Sie übermässig lieb.

SOPHIE: Das ist nicht wahr,
       Er hat mich nicht so lieb, als wie Er spricht.
       Vergess' Er mich!

OCTAVIAN: Ist mir um Sie und nur um Sie.

SOPHIE: Vergess' Er mich!

OCTAVIAN (*heftig*):
       Mag alles drunter oder drüber gehn!

SOPHIE (*leidenschaftlich*):
       Vergess' Er mich!

OCTAVIAN: Hab' keinen andern Gedanken nicht.
       Seh' alleweil Ihr lieb Gesicht.
             (*Fasst mit beiden Händen ihre Beiden.*)

SOPHIE (*schwach abwehrend*):
       Vergess' Er mich!

MARSCHALLIN (*ist indessen aufgestanden, bezwingt sich aber und setzt sich
    wieder, vor sich, getragen, gleichzeitig mit Octavian und Sophie*):
       Heut oder morgen oder den übernächsten Tag.
       Hab' ich mir's denn nicht vorgesagt?
       Das alles kommt halt über jede Frau.
       Hab' ich's den nicht gewusst?
       Hab' ich nicht ein Gelübde tan,
       Dass ich's mit einem ganz gefassten Herzen
       Ertragen werd' . . .
       Heut oder morgen oder den übernächsten Tag.
             (*Sie wischt sich die Augen, steht auf.*)

SOPHIA: I had hoped, truly, that your Lordship would quite otherwise
Befriend me, and would bring me help and comfort—

OCTAVIAN: What, are you then not glad?

SOPHIA (*angrily*):
And tell me, pray, what cause I have?

OCTAVIAN: Is it not cause enough that you are rid of him?

SOPHIA: Had it been done quite otherwise, 'twould have been well.
Angered and shamed am I—I feel the smart
Of every glance of scorn and pity that her Highness casts
at me.

OCTAVIAN: You wrong her, on my soul, by such a thought!

SOPHIA: Leave me in peace!

OCTAVIAN: That cannot be!

(*Seizes her hand.*)

SOPHIA: My father needs my help—

OCTAVIAN: My need is greater far—

SOPHIA: 'Tis lightly said—

OCTAVIAN: I love you with a mighty love—

SOPHIA: Nay—'tis not so
Your love is not as great as you declare—
Forget me quite—

OCTAVIAN: You are my all—you are my all.

SOPHIA: Forget me quite—

OCTAVIAN (*vehemently*):
Beside you, the whole world is nothing worth!

SOPHIA (*passionately*):
Forget me quite—

OCTAVIAN: My thoughts are ever of you alone!
Nothing but you I see.

(*Seizes both her hands in his.*)

SOPHIA (*defending herself weakly*):
Forget me quite—

PRINCESS: "Now or to-morrow: if not to-morrow, very soon"—
Did I not say the words myself?
There is no woman can escape her fate!
Did I not know the truth?
Did I not swear by all the Saints
That I with chastened heart and tranquil spirit
Would bear the blow...
"Now or to-morrow: if not to-morrow, very soon"—

(*Wipes her eyes and rises.*)

SOPHIE (*leise*):
>Die Fürstin da! Sie ruft lhn hin! So geh' Er doch.

OCTAVIAN (*ist ein paar Schritte gegen die Marschallin hingegangen, steht jetzt zwischen beiden, verlegen. Pause*).

SOPHIE (*in der Tür, unschlüssig, ob sie gehen oder bleiben soll*).

OCTAVIAN (*in der Mitte, dreht den Kopf von einer zur andern*).

MARSCHALLIN (*sieht seine Verlegenheit; ein trauriges Lächeln huscht über ihr Gesicht*).

SOPHIE (*an der Tür*):
>Ich muss hinein und fragen, wie's dem Vater geht.

OCTAVIAN: Ich muss jetzt was reden, und mir verschlagt's die Red'.

MARSCHALLIN: Der Bub', wie er verlegen da in der Mitten steht.

OCTAVIAN (*zu Sophie*):
>Bleib' Sie um alles hier.
>
>>(*Zur Marschallin.*)
>
>Wie, hat Sie was gesagt?

MARSCHALLIN (*geht, ohne Octavian zu beachten hinüber zu Sophie*).

OCTAVIAN (*tritt einen Schritt zurück*).

MARSCHALLIN (*steht vor Sophie, sieht sie prüfend, aber gütig an*).

SOPHIE (*in Verlegenheit, knickst*).

MARSCHALLIN: So schnell hat Sie ihn gar so lieb?

SOPHIE (*sehr schnell*):
>Ich weiss nicht, was Euer Gnaden meinen mit der Frag'.

MARSCHALLIN: Ihr blass Gesicht gibt schon die rechte Antwort drauf.

SOPHIE (*in grosser Schüchternheit und Verlegenheit, immer sehr schnell*):
>War gar kein Wunder, wenn ich blass bin, Euer Gnaden.
>Hab' einen grossen Schreck erlebt mit dem Herrn Vater.
>Gar nicht zu reden von gerechtem Emportement
>gegen den skandalösen Herrn Baron.
>Bin Euer Gnaden recht in Ewigkeit verpflichtet,
>Dass mit Dero Hilf' und Aufsicht —

MARSCHALLIN (*abwehrend*):
>Red' Sie nur nicht zu viel, Sie ist ja hübsch genug!
>Und gegen den Herrn Papa sein Uebel weiss ich etwa eine
>>Medizin.
>Ich geh' jetzt da hinein zu ihm und lad' ihn ein,
>Mit mir und Ihr und dem Herrn Grafen da
>In meinem Wagen heimzufahren — meint Sie nicht —
>Dass ihn das rekreieren wird und allbereits
>Ein wenig munter machen?

SOPHIE: Euer Gnaden sind die Güte selbst.

MARSCHALLIN: Und für die Blässe weiss vielleicht mein Vetter da die
>>Medizin.

SOPHIA (*softly*):

Her Highness! Look! She calls to you! Then go to her!

(*Octavian, after advancing a few steps towards the Princess, now stands unaided between the two.*)

(*Sophia in the doorway, hesitating whether to go or to remain.*)

(*Octavian, between them, turns his head from one to the other. The Princess notices his perplexity and a melancholy smile flits over her countenance.*)

SOPHIA (*by the door*):

I must go in and ask how my dear father does.

OCTAVIAN: Much fain would I tell her, but thought and language fail.

PRINCESS: The boy, look how he stands beside her there, perplexed
and pale.

OCTAVIAN (*to Sophia*):

Stay here, by all you love.

(*To the Princess.*)

How? did you speak to me?

(*The Princess, paying no heed to Octavian, crosses to Sophia and looks at her, critically but kindly. Sophia, much embarrassed, makes a curtsey. Octavian retreats a step.*)

PRINCESS: So quickly did you learn to love him?

SOPHIA (*very quickly*):

Indeed, Madam, your question I can hardly understand.

PRINCESS: Your cheek so pale gives me the answer plain enough.

SOPHIA (*very timid and embarrassed. Still very quickly*):

Small wonder too it is, your Highness, if I am pale.
But my dear father's sickness I was sorely frightened.
Did not that monster the Baron, too, give me just cause
For great offence by all that he has said and done?
And to your Highness I shall be most grateful always
Because your timely intervention—

PRINCESS (*deprecatorily*):

Waste not your words on me, your're pretty, that's enough!
And for your worthy father's humours, a most sovereign
cure I think I know.
I'll go, say a word to him, and bid him come
With me and you and Count Octavian,
In my own coach, and bring him homeward—Will that
not,
Think you, soon to his wonted health restore him quite,
And cheer his drooping spirits?

SOPHIA: Such graciousness puts me to shame.

PRINCESS: And for your poor pale cheeks I think my cousin there
will know the cure.

OCTAVIAN *(innig)* :

Marie Theres', wie gut Sie ist.
Marie Theres', ich weiss gar nicht. —

MARSCHALLIN *(mit einem undefinierbaren Ausdruck leise)* :

Ich weiss auch nix.
(Ganz tonlos.)
Gar nix.
(Winkt ihm zurückzubleiben.)

OCTAVIAN *(unschlüssig, als wollte er ihr nach)* :

Marie Theres'!

*(Marschallin bleibt in der Tür stehen. Octavian steht ihr zunächst,
Sophie weiter rechts.)*

MARSCHALLIN *(vor sich, zugleich mit Octavian und Sophie)* :

Hab' mir's gelobt, Ihn lieb zu haben in der richtigen **Weis'**.
Dass ich selbst Sein Lieb' zu einer andern
noch lieb hab! Hab' mir freilich nicht gedacht,
dass es so bald mir auferlegt sollt' werden!
(Seufzend.)
Es sind die mehrenen Dinge auf der Welt,
So dass sie ein's nicht glauben tät'.
Wenn man sie möcht' erzählen hör'n.
Alleinig wer's erlebt, der glaubt daran und weiss nicht
wie —
Da steht der Bub' und da steh' ich, und mit dem **fremden**
Mädel dort
Wird Er so glücklich sein, als wie halt Männer
Das Glücklichsein verstehen. In Gottes Namen.

OCTAVIAN *(zugleich mit der Marschallin und Sophie, erst vor sich, **dann**
Aug' in Aug' mit Sophie)* :

Es ist was kommen und ist was g'schehn,
Ich möcht' Sie fragen: darf's denn sein? und grad' **die**
Frag',
Die spür ich, dass sie mir verboten ist.
Ich möcht' Sie fragen: warum zittert was in mir? —
Ist denn ein grosses Unrecht geschehn? Und grad' an Sie
Darf ich die Frag' nicht tun — und dann seh' ich dich **an**,
Sophie, und seh' nur dich und spür' nur dich,
Sophie, und weiss von nichts als nur: dich hab' ich **lieb**.

SOPHIE *(zugleich mit der Marschallin und Octavian, erst vor sich, **dann**
Aug' in Aug' mit Octavian)* :

Mir ist wie in der Kirch'n, heilig ist mir und so bang.
Und doch ist mir unheilig auch! Ich weiss nicht, wie **mir**
ist.
(Ausdrucksvoll.)

OCTAVIAN (*with deep feeling*):

    Marie Theres', how good are you,
    Marie Theres', I do not know—

PRINCESS (*with an enigmatical expression, softly*):

    And I know nothing.

                                (*Quite toneless.*)

    Nothing—

            (*She makes a sign to him to remain.*)

OCTAVIAN (*uncertain, as if he wished to follow her*):

    Marie Theres'!

  (*The Princess remains standing in the door. Octavian stands next
  to her, Sophia further to the right.*)

PRINCESS (*to herself*):

    I made a vow to love him rightly as a good woman should,
    Nay, e'en to love the love he bore another
    I promised! But in truth I did not think
    That all so soon my vow would claim fulfilment.

                                 (*Sighing.*)

    Full many a thing is ordained in this world,
    Which we should scarce believe could be,
    If we heard others tell of them . . .
    But soon he whom they wound believes in them, and
                          knows not how—
    There stands the boy, and here stand I, and with his love,
                      new found this day,
    He will have happiness,
    After the manner of men, who think they know it all. 'Tis
                      done—so be it.

OCTAVIAN (*together with the Princess and Sophia, first aside, then gazing
into Sophia's eyes*):

    What has come o'er me, what has come to pass?
    I fain would ask her. Can it be? And just that question,
    I know I cannot ask of her.
    I fain would ask her: oh, why trembles all my soul?—
    Has bitter wrong, a sinful deed been done? And just
                      of her
    I may not ask the question—and then on your dear face
    I gaze, and see but you, and know but you,
    Sophia, and I know but this:
    You, you I love!

SOPHIA (*together with the Princess and Octavian, first aside, then gazing
into Octavian's eyes*):

    As one at worship, thoughts most holy fill my soul,
    And yet thoughts most unholy too possess me: I'm dis-
                      traught.

                      (*With much expression.*)

Ich möcht mich niederknien dort vor der Frau und möcht
ihr
was antun, denn ich spür', sie gibt mir ihn
und nimmt mir was von ihm zugleich.   Weiss gar nicht,
wie mir ist!
• Möcht' all's verstehen und möcht' auch nichts verstehen
Möcht fragen und nicht fragen, wird mir heiss und kalt.
Und spür nur dich und weiss nur eins: dich hab' ich lieb!

(Marschallin geht leise links hinein, die beiden bemerken es gar nicht. Octavian ist dicht an Sophie herangetreten, einen Augenblick später liegt sie in seinen Armen.)

OCTAVIAN *(zugleich mit Sophie)*:

Spür nur dich, spür nur dich allein
und dass wir beieinander sein!
Geht all's sonst wie ein Traum dahin
vor meinem Sinn!

SOPHIE *(zugleich mit Octavian)*:

Ist ein Traum, kann nicht wirklich sein,
dass wir zwei beieinander sein,
beieinand' für alle Zeit
und Ewigkeit!

OCTAVIAN *(ebenso)*:

War ein Haus wo, da warst du drein,
und die Leut' schicken mich hinein,
mich gradaus in die Seligkeit!
die waren g'scheit!

SOPHIE *(ebenso)*:

Kannst du lachen? Mir ist zur Stell'
bang wie an der himmlischen Schwell'!
Halt' mich, ein schwach Ding, wie ich bin,
sink' dir dahin!

(Sie muss sich an ihn lehnen. In diesem Augenblick öffnen die Faninalschen Lakaien die Tür und treten herein, jeder mit einem Leuchter. Durch die Tür kommt Faninal, die Marschallin an der Hand führend. Die beiden jungen stehen einen Augenblick verwirrt, dann machen sie ein tiefes Kompliment, das Faninal und die Marschallin erwidern. Faninal tupft Sophie väterlich gutmütig auf die Wange.)

FANINAL: Sind halt aso, die jungen Leut'!

MARSCHALLIN: Ja, ja.

(Faninal reicht der Marschallin die Hand, führt sie zur Mitteltür, die zugleich durch die Livree der Marschallin, darunter der kleine Neger, geöffnet wurde. Draussen hell, herinnen halb-dunkel, da die beiden Diener mit den Leuchtern der Marschallin voraustreten. Octavian und Sophie, allein im halbdunklen Zimmer, wiederholen leise.)

At yonder lady's feet I fain would kneel, yet would I toe
Fain harm her, for I feel that she gives him to me
And yet robs me of part of him. So strangely I'm per-
                                        plexed!
I would know all things, yet I fear to know the truth.
Now longing to ask, all now fearing, hot am I and cold.
And know but you and know but this one thing, that I
                                        love you!

*(The Princess goes quickly into the room on the left; the two others
do not notice her. Octavian has come quite near to Sophia. A
moment later she is clasped in his arms.)*

OCTAVIAN (*together with Sophia*):

You alone I know, only you
That you love me and I love you—
All besides like a vision seems
Of fleeting dreams.

SOPHIA (*together with Octavian*):

'Tis a dream of heaven: is it true,
That you love me and I love you?
Never in this world to part,
One soul, one heart!

OCTAVIAN (*louder*):

In a great house was your bower,
They sent me there in a happy hour
Straight to you and paradise,
Oh, they were wise.

SOPHIA: Dare you laugh so? I fear my fate,
As a soul that trembles at Heav'n's own gate!
Clasp me closer, friendless and weak,
Your arms I seek.

*(She leans on him for support. At this moment Faninal's footmen
open the door and enter, each carrying a candlestick. Faninal,
leading the Princess by the hand, enters through the door. The
two young people stand for a moment confused, then they make
a deep bow, which Faninal and the Princess return. Faninal
pats Sophia with paternal benevolence on the cheek.)*

FANINAL: 'Tis just their way,—youth will be young!

*(Faninal gives his hand to the princess, conducts her to the centre
door which the suite of the Princess, among them the little Black
Boy, at that moment throw open.)*

PRINCESS: Yes, yes.

*(Bright light outside, within a half-light, as the two Footmen with
the candlesticks precede the Princess.)*

OCTAVIAN (*zugleich mit Sophie*):

> Spür nur dich, spür nur dich allein
> und dass wir beieinander sein!
> Geht all's sonst wie ein Traum dahin
> vor meinem Sinn!

SOPHIE (*zugleich mit Octavian*):

> Ist ein Traum, kann nicht wirklich sein,
> dass wir zwei beieinander sein,
> beieinand' für alle Zeit
> und Ewigkeit!

(Sie sinkt an ihn hin, er küsst sie schnell. Ihr fällt, ohne dass sie es merkt, ihr Taschentuch aus der Hand. Dann laufen sie schnell, Hand in Hand, hinaus. Die Bühne bleibt leer, dann geht nochmals die Mitteltür auf. Herein kommt der kleine Neger, mit einer Kerze in der Hand, sucht das Taschentuch, findet es, hebt es auf, trippelt hinaus.)

OCTAVIAN (*dreamily*):

> You alone I know, only you,
> That you love me and I love you!
> All besides like a vision seems
> Of fleeting dreams.

SOPHIA (*dreamily*):

> 'Tis a dream, of heaven: is it true,
> That you love me and I love you?
> Never in this world to part—
> One soul, one heart.

OCTAVIAN and SOPHIA: I know you alone!

(She sinks into his arms. He kisses her quickly. Without her noticing it, her handkerchief drops from her hand. Then they run off quickly, hand in hand. The stage remains empty. Then the centre door is opened again. Through it comes the little Black Boy with a taper in his hand. Looks for the handkerchief— finds it—picks it up—trips out.)

(The curtain falls quickly.)

FURSTNER LIMITED, LONDON, W.1.

SALOME

MUSIC DRAMA IN ONE ACT
AFTER OSCAR WILDE'S POEM

MUSIC BY

RICHARD STRAUSS

VOCAL SCORE with German and English words
    (O. Singer) ....paper cover
Ditto ....cloth
VOCAL SCORE with French and Italian words
    (O. Singer) ....paper cover
VOCAL SCORE with French words.....................
Ditto ....cloth
PIANO SCORE with German and English text underneath
    (O. Taubmann) ....paper cover
Ditto ....cloth
PIANO SCORE with French and Italian text underneath.
    paper cover
Ditto ....cloth
PIANO SCORE at four hands, with German and French
    text underneath (O. Taubmann)........paper cover
SALOME'S DANCE for Orchestra.......................
SALOME'S DANCE for English or foreign Military Band.
SALOME'S DANCE for Piano solo......................
SALOME'S DANCE for Piano at four hands.............
SALOME'S DANCE for Two Pianos at four hands.......
FANTASIE (Selection) for Orchestra....................
Ditto, for small Orchestra............................
Ditto, for Parisian Orchestra.........................
Ditto, for Piano Solo.................................
SOLO SCENE OF SALOME for Voice and Piano with
    German words ....
SOLO SCENE OF SALOME for Voice and Piano with
    French and Italian words.......................
BOOKS OF WORDS. German............................
    Ditto   German with motives..............
    Ditto   German and English..............
    Ditto   French ....
    Ditto   Italian ....
    Ditto   Swedish ....
GUIDE THROUGH THE OPERA (O. Roese) with musical
    examples and Facsimile of a manuscript page of the
    original Orchestra Score ....